10656208
OOR WULLIE
IRONMONGER
BUCKETS
seats
D. C. Thomson & Co. Ltd. GLASGOW, LONDON, DUNDEE.
£1·80


A

OOR WULLIE
Who thinks that soap is nasty stuff—
Tae " wash " yer hands, a towel's enough . . ?
That's Wullie!
Who leaves footprints in wet cement
As off he goes on mischief bent . . ?
WET CEMENT
That's Wullie!
Who leaves the seat o' his best breeks
Snagged on the wire as fun he seeks . .?
NO FISHING KEEP OUT
That's Wullie!
A muddy ba', a snow-white sheet,
A mighty kick, then swift retreat . . .
That's Wullie!
Whose jaws work overtime when he
Sees what his Ma has baked for tea . . ?
Wullie!
And who, when it's time tae mak' ye laugh,
Does it all a treat, no' half . . ?
OOR WULLIE

Printed and Published in Great Britain by D. C. THOMSON & CO., LTD., 185 Fleet Street, London EC4A 2HS.

ISBN 0 85116 320 3

His itchy back makes things go wrong—
But he's " tickled " pink before too long!
I'M GOIN' TAE A PARTY TODAY. THERE'LL BE LOTS O' GAMES AN' PRIZES.
AWA' AN' GET YER HAIR CUT FOR THE PARTY.
ACH, A' RICHT!
LATER—
HAIRDRESSER
TCH! I'VE GOT HAIR DOON THE BACK O' MY NECK.
STOP THAT! YE'RE MAKIN' ME ITCH WORSE THAN EVER!
OCH, AWA'! THERE'S NOTHING LIKE A GUID SCRATCH ... MMM!
WE'LL PLAY AT MUSICAL STATUES FIRST!
BRAW! I'M REALLY GUID AT THIS! YE JIST STAND STILL WHEN THE MUSIC STOPS!
YOU'RE MOVING, WULLIE. YOU'RE FIRST TO SIT DOWN.
STILL
POISED
FIDGET!
ACH, THIS HAIR'S STILL TICKLIN' LIKE MAD!
NEVER MIND. HAVE A GLASS O' LEMONADE WHILE WE FINISH THE GAME.
TA!
OOH! IT'S ITCHIN' AGAIN!
MY GOOD CARPET!
I COULDNA HAUD STILL FOR THE TICKLIN'!
I'LL GIE MASEL' A BIT O' A SCRATCH ON THIS.
OW!
HA! HA! WULLIE'S PLAYIN' MUSICAL CHAIRS BY HIMSEL'!
LOOKS LIKE HE LOST, TOO!
LET'S PLAY HIDE AND SEEK, NOW.
GREAT! I'LL WIN THIS EASY!
THIS IS A BRAW HIDIN' PLACE.
CRIVVENS! I'M ITCHIN' AGAIN!
HELP!
CRASH!
JINGS! I THOUGHT MY TIME HAD COME, THERE!
PESKY HAIR! I'VE NO' WON A THING BECAUSE O' IT!
HERE YOU ARE, WULLIE. YOU'VE WON FIRST PRIZE.
EH? WHIT FOR?
FOR THE DISCO DANCING CONTEST!
THIS AULD HOOSE AIN'T GOT NO LINO ...
AAH ... THAT'S BETTER!

*He seeks it here, he seeks it there—*

*Oor Wullie's on the hunt for air!*

LET'S SEE WHIT I CAN FIND IN HERE.
I COULD HAE A GAME O' FITBA' WI' THIS, BUT I'LL NEED IT PUMPED UP, FIRST.
MR TUPP'LL NO' MIND IF I BLAW IT UP AT HIS FREE AIR PUMP.
JACK TUPP MOTOR ENGINEER
NOW, HOW DOES THIS THING WORK?
FREE AIR
ACH, HAUD YER HORSES! I'LL NO' BE A MINUTE!
PEEP! PEEP!
PARP!
TOOT!
WOULD YOU MIND GETTING AIR SOMEWHERE ELSE, WULLIE? MY CUSTOMERS AREN'T VERY PLEASED.
BUS STATION
WHIT'S WRANG, WULLIE?
I'M LOOKIN' FOR AIR.
JUST NIP ROOND THERE.
THAT'S THE AYR TOUR.
ACH, YE KEN FINE THAT'S NO' WHIT I'M AFTER!
AYR BURNS COUNTRY
DID I 'EAR YOU SAY YOU WANTED 'AIR? LOOK OVER 'ERE, SONNY.
YOU'LL GET LOTS OF 'AIR ON THE FLOOR IN THE 'AIRDRESSER'S.
GENT'S HAIRDRESSER
AYE, BUT IT'S AIR FOR MY BA' I WANT.
HE COULDNAE HELP IT, HE WIS ENGLISH. SOME ENGLISH FOWK DINNA HALF SPEAK FUNNY.
SEE—JUST A BAG O' HOT AIR!
JUST WHIT I NEED!
VOTE FOR ME, AN' WE'LL HAE MEALY PUDDENS AND FISH SUPPERS ON THE NATIONAL HEALTH . . .
I HEAR YE'VE A LOT OF HOT AIR TAE SPARE. COULD YE BLAW UP MY BA'?
VOTE FOR HONEST MAC.
HE'S NO' PLEASED.
GIVE HIM AIR! GIVE HIM AIR!
GIE ME SOME AN' A' . . . OOPS!
HE'S FAINTED. HE JUST OPENED HIS ELECTRICITY BILL.
WELL, IT LOOKS LIKE THERE'LL BE NAE FITBA' FOR ME THE DAY.
HEY, WULLIE! ARE YE COMIN' IN TAE PLAY? MY UNCLE'S BROUGHT ME A BRAW PRESENT.
LOOK—BLAW FITBA'! GREAT, EH?
HA-HA! WE PLAYED ANYWAY, AN' I WON EIGHTY-NINE GOALS TAE SIXTY-FIVE!

*It's easy to tell—*

*That Wullie can't spell!*

HE'S AT SCHOOL.
WILLIAM, YOUR SPELLING IS APPALLING!
YOU SPELL WEATHER "WETHIR"! THAT'S THE WORST SPELL OF WEATHER WE'VE HAD IN A LONG TIME!
JINGS! NO' THAT AULD JOKE AGAIN!
AFTER SCHOOL—
I HOPE YER GOALKEEPIN'S BETTER THAN YER SPELLIN', WULLIE. MIND YE'RE PLAYIN' FOR GOWRIE STREET THISTLE THE NICHT.
OH, AYE.
HEY, WULLIE! I'LL GIE YE TWENTY PENCE IF YE'LL PAINT A "NO ADMITTANCE" SIGN FOR ME.
GREAT!
ACH, I CANNAE SPELL "ADMITTANCE", BUT I'LL DAE SOMETHIN' JUST AS GUID.
FINISHED! I COULDNAE SPELL THAT BIG WORD, SO I CHANGED IT TO TAE "KEEP OUT"!
CLEVER LAD.
HUH! LOOK AT THIS SPELLIN'! I'LL HAVE TAE DAE IT AGAIN MASEL'. NAE TWENTY PENCE FOR YOU!
KEEP OWT.
OH, WULLIE. MIND THOSE JUMBLE SALE POSTERS YE DID FOR ME?
AYE, THEY WERE BRAW, EH?
THERE'S NAE SAILIN' OR BOATS INVOLVED.
ACH, AWA'! WHIT ABOOT THE JUNK?
JUMBLE SAIL.
ROCER
CAN YE PAINT A SIGN ON THE INSIDE O' MY WINDIE, WULLIE?
SURE!
YE'LL HAVE TAE BE CAREFUL NO' TAE GET THE LETTERS THE WRONG WAY ROOND.
DINNA WORRY. JUST LEAVE IT TAE ME.
LATER—
COME AN' SEE—A' THE LETTERIN' LOOKS FINE.
GROCER
THE LETTERS ARE FINE, BUT YE'VE MADE A DOG'S DINNER O' THE SPELLIN'!
AYE, A COLLIE DOG'S DINNER!
COLLIEFLOWERS 25P
CRIVVENS! I FORGOT ABOOT THE FITBA' MATCH! I'D BETTER RUN HAME FOR MY GEAR.
HOPE I'M NO' TOO LATE.
HUH! WHAUR WERE YOU?
THE GAME'S LANG SINCE FINISHED.
WE LOST TEN NIL WITHOUT A PROPER GOALIE! LET'S GET HIM, LADS!
CALM DOON, LADS. IT'S NO' THAT BAD.
LET'S GO INTAE THE PAVILION AN' DISCUSS THIS.
PIECE TALKS KEEP OOT!
LOOKS LIKE WULLIE'S SPELLING IS STILL AS BAD AS EVER!
YE'RE WRONG THERE. I'VE MADE UP WI' MY PALS AGAIN BY GIVIN' THEM THE PIECES THAT MA MADE FOR ME TAE EAT AFTER THE GAME.
ACH, I'LL JUST LEAVE SPELLIN' TAE WITCHES—THEY'RE BETTER AT IT THAN ME!

*There's trouble for you-know-who—*

*On a bicycle built for two!*

MICHTY ME! ALEC'S AWA' TAE WORK WITHOOT HIS PIECE AGAIN.
DINNA WORRY, MRS McGOWAN, I'LL TAK' IT TAE HIM.
BUT, WULLIE . . .
IT'S OKAY, I KEN WHAUR HE WORKS!
ACH, HE'S GONE OWER THE LEVEL CROSSIN', AN' NOW THE GATES ARE SHUT!
HERE COMES THE TRAIN. WHIT A TIME IT'S TAKIN'.
HOW ABOUT A LIFT, SANDY?
SURE, WULLIE. HOP ON! YE'LL HAVE TAE DAE YER SHARE O' PEDALLIN' THOUGH.
PECH! GASP! PECH!
WAIT A MINUTE! THIS ISNAE THE ROAD TAE MR McGOWAN'S WORK!
HOLD IT, SANDY! I'LL HAVE TAE GET AFF HERE!
ACH, NOW I'VE GOT TAE GET UP THIS BRAE ON MY OWN!
ECK, GIVE'S A LIFT, I'M IN A HURRY.
OOPS!
HUH! NOW I'LL HAVE TAE RUN A' THE WAY.
HEY, WHIT ABOOT MY WHEEL?
ACH, CLAIM IT AFF YER INSURANCE.
I'LL TAK' A SHORT-CUT OWER THE BURN.
WHIT?
HELP M'BOAB, I'M DROOKIT!
EVENTUALLY—
CAUGHT YE AT LAST! I'VE GOT YER PIECE HERE, MR McGOWAN.
WORKS ENTRANCE
NO, I'VE GOT IT HERE, WULLIE.
YOU'VE GOT IT? THEN WHIT'S IN HERE?
CLOTHES PEGS?
AYE, I TRIED TO TELL YE, WULLIE. YE TOOK THE WRANG BAG!
WHIT A SCUNNER! STILL, THE CLOTHES PEGS CAME IN HANDY!

*A BIG let-down—*

*From Jingo the clown!*

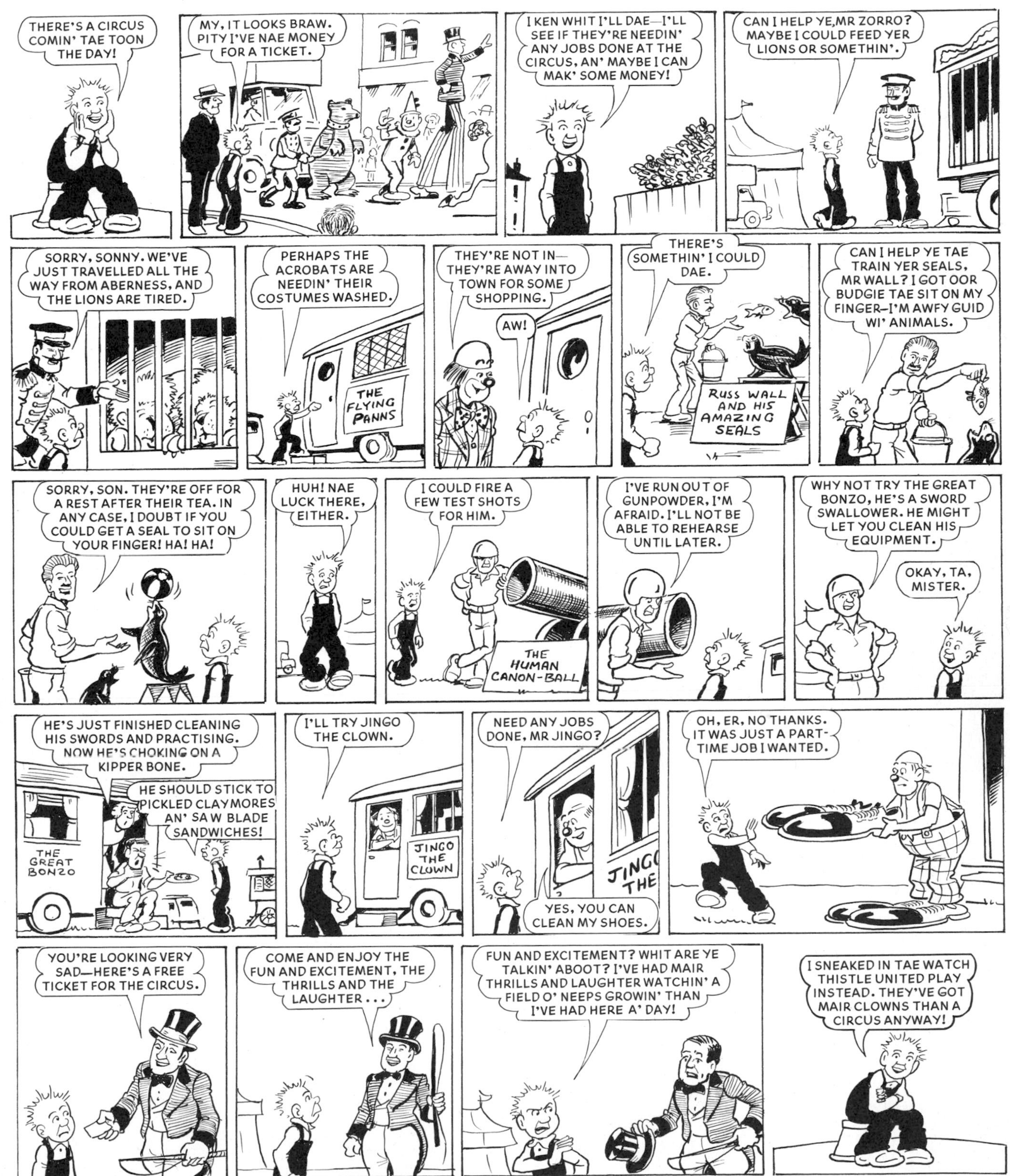
THERE'S A CIRCUS COMIN' TAE TOON THE DAY!
MY, IT LOOKS BRAW. PITY I'VE NAE MONEY FOR A TICKET.
I KEN WHIT I'LL DAE—I'LL SEE IF THEY'RE NEEDIN' ANY JOBS DONE AT THE CIRCUS, AN' MAYBE I CAN MAK' SOME MONEY!
CAN I HELP YE, MR ZORRO? MAYBE I COULD FEED YER LIONS OR SOMETHIN'.
SORRY, SONNY. WE'VE JUST TRAVELLED ALL THE WAY FROM ABERNESS, AND THE LIONS ARE TIRED.
PERHAPS THE ACROBATS ARE NEEDIN' THEIR COSTUMES WASHED.
THE FLYING PANNS
THEY'RE NOT IN— THEY'RE AWAY INTO TOWN FOR SOME SHOPPING.
AW!
THERE'S SOMETHIN' I COULD DAE.
RUSS WALL AND HIS AMAZING SEALS
CAN I HELP YE TAE TRAIN YER SEALS, MR WALL? I GOT OOR BUDGIE TAE SIT ON MY FINGER—I'M AWFY GUID WI' ANIMALS.
SORRY, SON. THEY'RE OFF FOR A REST AFTER THEIR TEA. IN ANY CASE, I DOUBT IF YOU COULD GET A SEAL TO SIT ON YOUR FINGER! HA! HA!
HUH! NAE LUCK THERE, EITHER.
I COULD FIRE A FEW TEST SHOTS FOR HIM.
THE HUMAN CANON-BALL
I'VE RUN OUT OF GUNPOWDER, I'M AFRAID. I'LL NOT BE ABLE TO REHEARSE UNTIL LATER.
WHY NOT TRY THE GREAT BONZO, HE'S A SWORD SWALLOWER. HE MIGHT LET YOU CLEAN HIS EQUIPMENT.
OKAY, TA, MISTER.
HE'S JUST FINISHED CLEANING HIS SWORDS AND PRACTISING. NOW HE'S CHOKING ON A KIPPER BONE.
HE SHOULD STICK TO PICKLED CLAYMORES AN' SAW BLADE SANDWICHES!
THE GREAT BONZO
I'LL TRY JINGO THE CLOWN.
JINGO THE CLOWN
NEED ANY JOBS DONE, MR JINGO?
JINGO THE
YES, YOU CAN CLEAN MY SHOES.
OH, ER, NO THANKS. IT WAS JUST A PART-TIME JOB I WANTED.
YOU'RE LOOKING VERY SAD—HERE'S A FREE TICKET FOR THE CIRCUS.
COME AND ENJOY THE FUN AND EXCITEMENT, THE THRILLS AND THE LAUGHTER . . .
FUN AND EXCITEMENT? WHIT ARE YE TALKIN' ABOOT? I'VE HAD MAIR THRILLS AND LAUGHTER WATCHIN' A FIELD O' NEEPS GROWIN' THAN I'VE HAD HERE A' DAY!
I SNEAKED IN TAE WATCH THISTLE UNITED PLAY INSTEAD. THEY'VE GOT MAIR CLOWNS THAN A CIRCUS ANYWAY!

*This new lad knows all the tricks—*

*But see Wull land him in a fix!*

HI, LADS, I'M NEW AROOND HERE. CAN I PLAY WI' YOU THREE?
AYE, SURE.
HOW ABOOT A BOXING CONTEST? AWA' AN' FETCH YER GLOVES.
RIGHT, WE'RE A' READY. WHAUR'S YOUR GLOVES?
I'M NO' USIN' ANY. I'M WAITIN' FOR THIS WEDDIN'!
SCRAMBLE!
HEE-HEE! I KENT THERE WIS A SCRAMBLE —AN' THEY CANNAE PICK UP ANY O' THE MONEY! I'M REAL CRAFTY.
LET'S PLAY HIDE AN' SEEK AT MY HOOSE. I'LL BE OOT FIRST.
21...22... 23...
OH, WHERE HAVE YOUR NEW FRIENDS GONE? I BROUGHT SOME TOFFEE FOR THEM.
ER, I CANNA FIND THEM.
I'LL TAK' THEIR SHARE, THOUGH.
MMMM... GREAT TOFFEE! CRAFTY, EH?
LET'S PLAY KNIGHTS.
OKAY.
TAK' THAT, YE VARLET! COME ON, MEN!
THAT'S IT, MEN, SHOW NO MERCY!
GOOD BOY. HERE'S THE MONEY I PROMISED YE FOR GETTIN' RID O' THOSE WEEDS.
HUMPH! IT'S TIME WE GOT OOR AIN BACK ON THIS LAD.
WELL, YE'RE CERTAINLY A CRAFTY PERSON.
AYE, WHEN IT COMES TAE CRAFT, THERE'S NAEBODY BETTER THAN ME.
IS THAT SO? COME WITH ME.
EH?
I'M ALWAYS DELIGHTED TO ENCOURAGE SOMEONE KEEN ON CRAFT.
HEE-HEE! THAT'S MISS WICKET, THE CRAFT TEACHER AT OOR SCHOOL.

*Wull does his best to guard that box—*

*But in the end, it gives him shocks.*

HEY, WULLIE! COULD YE DAE A WEE JOB FOR ME?
SURE, MR JOHNSTONE.
HERE'S THIRTY PENCE. TAK' THESE LETTERS ROOND TAE BILL RAMSAY AT FORTY-SEVEN GRAHAM STREET.
OKAY!
I WONDER WHY HE DIDNAE JIST POST THE LETTERS?
MAYBE HE WIS TRYIN' TAE SAVE MONEY . . .
LOOK OUT, WULLIE!
JINGS! I MUSTN'T LET THE LETTERS GET WET OR THE INK'LL RUN AN' MR RAMSAY WINNA BE ABLE TAE READ THEM.
CAUTION BURST WATER MAIN.
I'D BETTER DRY OUT THE WRAPPING. CAN YE POINT YER BLOW-LAMP AT MY PARCEL, MR BURNS?
CABLE
THERE YE GO, WULLIE.
TA!
HA-HA! THERE'S ANE IN THE PANTS FOR YE, WULLIE! I COULDNAE RESIST IT!
OW!
YE BIG PUDDEN! IF I WISNAE ON AN IMPORTANT MISSION I'D FLATTEN YE!
CRIVVENS! IF IT'S NO' ONE THING IT'S ANOTHER.
GET AFF, YE BRUTE. YE'RE NO' GETTIN' TAE CHEW UP MY LETTERS.
THAT SHOULD KEEP YE OOT!
PARK
I'LL HAE A WEE REST. THERE'S NAE WATER MAINS NOR DOGS TAE BOTHER ME HERE.
HEY, WATCH IT, WIFIE.
JINGS, THAT WIS CLOSE. YE'D HAVE CRUSHED MY LETTERS TAE A PULP.
WHIT?
I'LL CRUSH YOU TAE A PULP, YE CHEEKY WEE DEVIL.
THIS IS GRAHAM STREET, NOW WHERE'S NUMBER FORTY-SEVEN?
HELP M'BOAB! IT'S THE RIO CINEMA!
47 RIO CI
ARE THOSE MY LETTERS, WULLIE?
DAE YE LIKE MY NEW WATER-RESISTANT, UNBREAKABLE, EVERLASTING LETTERS FOR THE CINEMA SIGN? THE OTHERS WERE GETTIN' AWFY TATTY.
'BABY FACE' STARRING JOHN WEAN ALL THIS WEEK
ACH, SO THEY'RE THAT SORT O' LETTERS!
RIO CINEMA
HUH!

*Your face will fill with laughter creases—*

*When Wull's pals do their party pieces!*

HE'S AT THE THEATRE!
HA-HA! WHIT A LAUGH!
THAT RIKKI MILROY WAS GREAT. I THINK I'LL BE A COMIC WI' MY AIN SHOW.
THEATRE
I'LL START AUDITIONS STRAIGHT AWAY.
NEW STARS WANTED FOR WULLIE'S VARIETY SHOW.
I'M A DAB HAND WI' THE MOOTHIE.
YOU CAN SAW ME IN HALF, IF YOU LIKE, WILLIAM.
SOAPY, GET SOME CLOTHES POLES. BOAB, WE'LL NEED SOME CURTAINS.
SOON—
LADEEZ AND GEN'ELMEN! WELCOME TAE WULLIE'S WONDER SHOW. OOR FIRST ACT THIS AFTERNOON IS THE AMAZING ECHO—MAESTRO O' THE MOOTHIE.
I'D LIKE TAE GIE YE "THE ROAD AN' THE MILES TAE DUNDEE".
IT'S THE ROAD AN' THE MILES TAE AUCHENTOGLE FOR YOU—WE'RE VISITIN' YER GRANNY. COME OWER HERE AT ONCE!
SORRY ABOOT THAT, A'BODY. NEXT WE'VE GOT THE STUNNING PRIMOSE "TWO-PIECE" PATERSON, WHO'LL BE SAWN IN HALF BY SOAPY SAWYER.
PRIMROSE IS IN A TRICK CABINET. IT'S A'RICHT, REALLY!
WHIT ARE YE DAEIN' WI' MY SAW? I'M NEEDIN' IT TAE FIX THE BUNKER.
JINGS! THIS IS AWFY!
ER—WELL, THAT WIS THE AMAZIN' VANISHIN' SAW TRICK. NOO THE McTURK SISTERS WILL DAE SOME HIGHLAND DANCIN'.
SO THAT'S WHAUR MY BREAD KNIVES ARE!
WELL, THAT'S THE HIGHLAND DANCIN' SCUPPERED.
AN' NOO WHIT YE'VE A BEEN WAITIN' FOR! THE STAR O' THE SHOW—ME!
DID YE HEAR ABOOT THE WOMAN WHO THOUGHT YE GOT STEEL WOOL FROM HYDRAULIC RAMS?
...SO THE OPTICIAN SAYS TAE ME, "HAVE YER EYES EVER BEEN CHECKED?", AN' I SAYS, "NA', THEY'VE AYE BEEN BLUE!"
BOAB! GET MY CURTAINS DOON FROM THERE THIS MINUTE!
CRIVVENS! IT'S MY MA!
...AN' THEN THERE WAS THE ICE CREAM VAN THAT MELTED...
GIVE ME BACK MY CLOTHES POLES RIGHT NOW! I CANNA GET MY WASHIN' HUNG OOT!
OH, ER, A'RICHT, MA.
HELP M'BOAB! IT'S RIKKI MILROY HIMSEL'!
HULLO, WULLIE. I SAW YER SHOW.
I LIKED A' YER JOKES, WULLIE. I'LL GIE YE FIFTY PENCE EACH FOR THEM.
GREAT!
I'LL NO' BE A COMIC AFTER A'. I THINK I'LL BE A SCRIPTWRITER INSTEAD.

*This hat's a handy thing indeed—*

*It's everywhere, 'cept on his heid!*

LOOK AT THAT! THERE'S AN AULD HELMET BEIN' THROWN OOT. THAT COULD BE USEFUL.
ACH, MY TEA CAN'S LEAKIN'!
LOOKS LIKE TAM'S HAEIN' A SPOT O' BOTHER.
IT'S A'RICHT, TAM. WE CAN WASH OOT MY HELMET AN' USE THAT.
SMASHIN', WULLIE.
AYE, IT'S BILIN' UP NICELY.
THAT WIS A BRILLIANT IDEA, WULLIE. TUCK IN.
TA!
MMM... THAT WIS BRAW.
FAIR GROUND
DAD! DAD! THE BAG'S GOIN' TAE BURST!
A LEAKIN' BAG, EH?
HERE, YE CAN STICK YER FISH IN MY HELMET TILL YE GET IT HAME.
THANKS. JUST IN TIME, TOO!
TAK' THIS, WULLIE. YE'RE A BRIGHT LAD.
THANKS, MISTER.
ACH, THERE'S WEE HAMISH RUNNIN' AWA' AGAIN.
DINNA WORRY, I'LL STOP HIM!
EH?
HELP M'BOAB!
MAIR QUICK THINKIN', EH, WULLIE? HERE'S A BONUS FOR YE.
IT'S A DOG'S LIFE!
THAT'S NO' BAD. A BRAW FEED, AN' TWENTY PENCE, ALL FROM AN AULD HELMET.
Wullies Hoose
LET'S SEE... I COULD BUY SWEETS, OR A BEANO AN' A DANDY...
WATCH OOT, WULLIE. YE'VE KNOCKED THE PLANT OOT O' MY HANDS!
OUCH!
WHY DID YE NO' WEAR YER HELMET? THAT WOULD'VE SAVED YE.
CRIVVENS! I WIS SO BUSY USIN' IT FOR OTHER THINGS, I NEVER THOUGHT O' WEARIN' IT!
PAW GAVE ME TEN PENCE FOR THAT IDEA. NO' BAD, EH? THAT'S HOW TAE MAK' MONEY—USE YER HEID, AN' USE YER HAT!

*A swivel bucket? My, that's posh—*

*But when oor lad sits doon . . . oh, gosh!*

HE'S HAVIN' HIS BREAKFAST
CRIVVENS! I NEVER REALISED MY BUCKET WIS GETTIN' SO SCRUFFY!
I'LL HAVE TAE GET A NEW SEAT.
FURNITURE STORE
YES, YOUNG MAN, WHAT CAN I DO FOR YOU?
I'M LOOKIN' FOR A NEW SEAT.
WELL, THIS IS OOR SNOOZE-EASY ROCKING-CHAIR.
AND HERE'S OUR SUPER-SWIVEL EXECUTIVE ARMCHAIR.
OR THERE'S ALWAYS OUR DE LUXE RELAXATION ARM-CHAIR WITH ITS OWN BUILT-IN HEATING PAD FOR COLD WINTER NIGHTS.
ER, HAVE YE ANY-THIN' FOR TWENTY-THREE PENCE?
OUT!
ACH, I ONLY ASKED.
I'LL JIST HAVE TAE MAK' MY AIN COMFY CHAIR.
THERE, HOW'S THAT? A ROCKIN' BUCKET.
SO THAT'S WHAUR MY CUDDY WENT TAE!
HERE COMES TROUBLE!
GET YER AIN HORSE, WULLIE!
THAT'S BETTER. MY AIN SWIVEL BUCKET.
NOW TAE TRY IT OOT.
OW!
IF I FILL IT WI' HOT WATER AN' PUT A LID ON IT, I'LL HAE A HEATED SEAT.
AW, JINGS! IT'S SPRUNG A LEAK!
HULLO, WULLIE. HERE'S YER BUCKET BACK. I BORROWED IT TAE CLEAN THE WINDIES, AN' LEFT YE THAT AULD LEAKY ANE TAE SIT ON.
SMASHIN'! YE CANNAE BEAT A GUID BUCKET FOR SITTIN' ON.

# *There's danger on the Whinny Braes—*

# *Or so oor climbing hero says!*

THERE'S JOCK WILLIAMSON. HE MUST BE AWA' UP THE HILLS AGAIN.
I'M CLIMBIN' BEN-BOGLE TODAY, WULLIE. IT'S AWFY HARD GOIN', YE KEN. YE'VE GOT TAE BE TOUGH TAE GET TAE THE TOP O' BEN BOGLE.
JINGS.
WELL, CHEERIO THE NOO, WULLIE.
'BYE, JOCK.
I THINK I'LL TRY A WEE BIT CLIMBIN' MASEL'.
PITY ABOUT MY HAVERSACK STRAPS BREAKIN'. I'LL JIST HAVE TAE USE THIS BIT O' ROPE INSTEAD.
WHINNY BRAES, HERE I COME.
PHEW! YE'VE GOT TAE BE TOUGH TAE CONQUER WHINNY BRAES.
I'LL NEED SOME ENERGY. THIS STICK O' DRUMTOGLE ROCK SHOULD DAE FINE.
OOYAH! MY TOOTH!
JINGS, THAT WIS SORE. I THINK I'VE CRACKED A TOOTH. STILL, YE'VE GOT TAE BE TOUGH. I'LL CARRY ON.
HEY, YOU. WHIT'S A YOUNG LAD LIKE YOU DAEIN' ROAMIN' AROUND? YE SHOULD BE AT SCHOOL.
ACH AWA', YE AULD GROUSE! IT'S SATURDAY!
MICHTY ME, THIS IS A STEEP BIT.
HELP M'BOAB. THE ROPE'S SNAPPED. I'LL HAVE TAE CARRY THE HAVERSACK.
GASP! THIS IS THIRSTY WORK.
AHA! THERE'S TONI'S ICE CREAM VAN. I THINK I'LL PAY HIM A VISIT.
HELLO, JOCK. HOW DID YE GET ON CLIMBIN' BEN BOGLE?
ICE CRE
OH, IT WIS AWFY, WULLIE. FIRST I GOT INJURED ON A BIG LUMP O' ROCK . . .
. . . THEN I CAME ACROSS AN ANGRY AULD GROUSE . . .
. . . NEXT THING, MY ROPE BROKE, AN' IN THE END I HAD TAE TURN BACK BECAUSE O' ICE.
THAT'S AMAZIN'. THAT'S EXACTLY WHIT HAPPENED TAE ME WHEN I WENT UP THE WHINNY BRAES.
ICE ON THE WHINNY BRAES?
JOCK SAYS HE'S GOIN' TAE TRY THE WHINNY BRAES NEXT TIME.

*Lassies, teachers and P.C.'s—*

*They're all wearing dungarees!*

JINGS! THERE'S ANOTHER LAD WEARIN' DUNGAREES! WHIT A CHEEK!
HEY, YOU!
YES?
HELP M'BOAB! A LASSIE! ER, SORRY, I THOUGHT YE WERE SOMEBODY ELSE.
LASSIES IN DUNGAREES? WHIT'S THE WORLD COMIN' TAE?
CRIVVENS! THERE'S DAPHNE BROON WEARIN' DUNGAREES AN' A'!
THIS IS GETTIN' WORSE! SOON A'BODY WILL BE WEARIN' THEM!
MICHTY ME! THERE'S MY SCHOOL TEACHER. HE'S WEARIN' DUNGAREES— AN' HE'S CARRYIN' A BUCKET!
IT'S AWFY. SOON I'LL LOOK JIST LIKE A'BODY ELSE!
WELL, THAT'S THE CAR WASHED. NOW I CAN TAKE THESE OFF AND PUT THE BUCKET IN THE SHED.
AW, NO!
NOW THE BOBBIES ARE WEARIN' DUNGAREES AN' A'!
SOON THERE'LL BE THOOSANDS O' THESE COPYCATS!
THAT'S MY GARDENIN' BREEKS WASHED AN' HUNG UP TAE DRY. HULLO—THAT LOOKS LIKE WULLIE OVER THERE.
ACH, THERE'S NAE JUSTICE. I'M THE ANE THAT WEARS DUNGAREES. A'BODY ELSE CANNAE WEAR THEN AN' A'!
IT'S JIST NO' FAIR!
OOPS! NOW I'VE BROKEN A WINDIE!
COME BACK HERE, YE WEE MONKEY!
NAE CHANCE!
OKAY, WULLIE, OWN UP. ONE BROKEN GREENHOUSE WINDIE. YE NEEDNAE DENY IT WIS YOU.
Wullie's Shed.
BUT HOW DID YE KEN I DID IT?
EASY, I HAD A PERFECT DESCRIPTION. A WEE LAD IN DUNGAREES . . .
. . . IT COULDNAE POSSIBLY BE ANYBODY ELSE. YE STAND OOT A MILE IN THOSE BREEKS!
WID YE BELIEVE IT?

*. . . but in the end, wee Wull believes—*

*The fortune told in his tea leaves!*

HE'LL BE HAME FOR HIS DINNER SOON.

I'M HAME, MA! OH, HELLO, MRS Mc NAB.

HELLO, WULLIE.

LATER—

MRS Mc NAB WILL READ YER CUP AFORE YE GO BACK TAE SCHOOL, WULLIE. SHE CAN TELL YER FORTUNE, YE KEN.

A'RICHT!

I SEE YOUR FUTURE INVOLVING MANY LINES. THEY ARE GOING TO MAKE YOU VERY UNHAPPY.

REALLY?

CHEERIO, THEN. I'M OFF TAE SCHOOL.

FORTUNE TELLING—WHIT A LOAD O' JUNK!

HUH! LINES WILL MAK' ME UNHAPPY, EH? THERE'S BILL DOW WI' A FISHIN' LINE. THAT'LL NO' MAK' ME SAD.

HI, WULLIE. LIKE TAE TRY OOT MY NEW ROD?

SURE, BILL.

JINGS! THAT'S A WHOPPER!

AYE, IT'S A CRACKER!

'BYE, BILL.

WELL, THAT DIDNAE MAK' ME UNHAPPY.

HOW ABOOT LETTIN' ME PAINT SOME O' YER LINES, MR MACKAY?

I'D BE GLAD IF YE COULD, WULLIE. I'M FAIR PUGGLED.

THIS IS NO' MAKIN' ME UNHAPPY.

'BYE, MR MACKAY!

THANKS FOR YER HELP, WULLIE.

HEY, WULLIE! FANCY TAKIN' THE ENGINE UP THE LINE? THE INSPECTOR'S OFF TODAY.

GREAT!

YER WEE SCENIC RAILWAY IS JIST BRAW, MR ELLIS.

THANKS, I'D BETTER AWA' TAE SCHOOL NOW.

WELL, THE RAILWAY LINE DIDNAE MAK' ME UNHAPPY.

CRIVVENS! LOOK AT THE TIME! I'M AWFY LATE!

YOU'RE LATE AGAIN, WILLIAM. I'M GOING TO PUNISH YOU . . .

MICHTY ME. THIS'LL BE THE LINES MRS Mc NAB WIS ON ABOOT.

. . . BUT YOU'LL BE PUNISHED IN A NEW WAY. GO TO MISS MACLEOD'S CLASS AND HELP OUT THERE THIS AFTERNOON.

MISS MACLEOD TEACHES DOMESTIC SCIENCE. I'LL LIKELY GET TAE TEST THEIR BAKIN' AN' A'THING. MRS Mc NAB WIS WRONG!

IN TROUBLE AGAIN, WILLIAM? GO AND HELP THE GIRLS OVER THERE.

AW, NO!

A WASHIN' LINE!

HUH! I'M GOIN' TAE INSIST ON TEA BAGS IN FUTURE!

*Well, well, well, ye'll never guess—*

*What goes wi' Wull, tae Auntie Bess!*

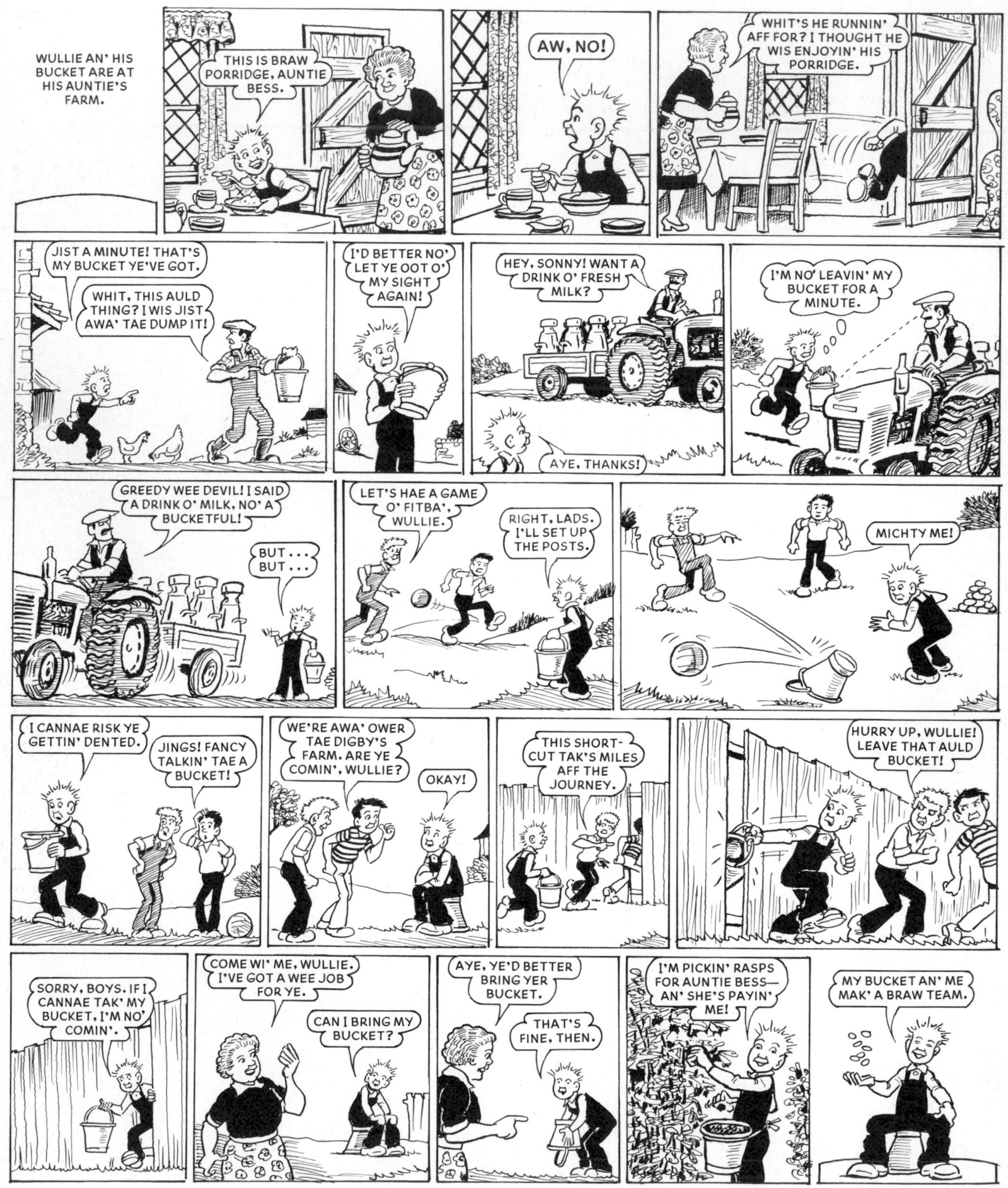

WULLIE AN' HIS BUCKET ARE AT HIS AUNTIE'S FARM.
THIS IS BRAW PORRIDGE, AUNTIE BESS.
AW, NO!
WHIT'S HE RUNNIN' AFF FOR? I THOUGHT HE WIS ENJOYIN' HIS PORRIDGE.
JIST A MINUTE! THAT'S MY BUCKET YE'VE GOT.
WHIT, THIS AULD THING? I WIS JIST AWA' TAE DUMP IT!
I'D BETTER NO' LET YE OOT O' MY SIGHT AGAIN!
HEY, SONNY! WANT A DRINK O' FRESH MILK?
AYE, THANKS!
I'M NO' LEAVIN' MY BUCKET FOR A MINUTE.
GREEDY WEE DEVIL! I SAID A DRINK O' MILK, NO' A BUCKETFUL!
BUT . . . BUT . . .
LET'S HAE A GAME O' FITBA', WULLIE.
RIGHT, LADS. I'LL SET UP THE POSTS.
MICHTY ME!
I CANNAE RISK YE GETTIN' DENTED.
JINGS! FANCY TALKIN' TAE A BUCKET!
WE'RE AWA' OWER TAE DIGBY'S FARM. ARE YE COMIN', WULLIE?
OKAY!
THIS SHORT-CUT TAK'S MILES AFF THE JOURNEY.
HURRY UP, WULLIE! LEAVE THAT AULD BUCKET!
SORRY, BOYS. IF I CANNAE TAK' MY BUCKET, I'M NO' COMIN'.
COME WI' ME, WULLIE. I'VE GOT A WEE JOB FOR YE.
CAN I BRING MY BUCKET?
AYE, YE'D BETTER BRING YER BUCKET.
THAT'S FINE, THEN.
I'M PICKIN' RASPS FOR AUNTIE BESS— AN' SHE'S PAYIN' ME!
MY BUCKET AN' ME MAK' A BRAW TEAM.

*Wullie's latest ploy's just great—*

*Till he's joined by a heavyweight!*

HE'S AT THE PICTURES.
THAT WIS BRAW! DID YE SEE THAT APE MAN SWING A' THE WAY THROUGH THE JUNGLE ON CREEPERS? HIS FEET NEVER TOUCHED THE GROUND.
CINEMA
NOW SHOWING THE APE MAN
ACH, THAT'S EASY. ANYONE COULD DAE THAT.
OKAY, SMART ALEC, I'LL BUY YE A HAGGIS SUPPER IF YE CAN GET ACROSS TOON WITHOOT TOUCHIN' THE GROUND.
YE'RE ON!
THERE'S A HANDY CREEPER, I'LL START HERE.
OW!
YOU ROTTEN BULLY!
OOPS! MAYBE I'D BETTER START SOMEWHERE ELSE.
THERE'S PLENTY O' TREES IN THE PARK. I'LL START IN THERE INSTEAD.
PARK
YOU TWA CAN JIST ABOOT TURN AN' MARCH RICHT OOT O' HERE. YE'RE BAITH BANNED FROM THE PARK SINCE YE PLAYED KEEPIE-UP WI' MY BAG O' SANDWICHES!
IT DOESNAE LOOK LIKE YE'RE GOIN' TAE MAK' IT ACROSS TOON WITHOOT YER FEET TOUCHIN' THE GROUND, WULLIE.
ACH, JIST YOU WAIT.
DAWSON AVENUE'S THE PLACE, BOAB! LOOK AT A' THESE GREENIE POLES!
I'LL USE THE WASHIN' LINES.
SEE? NAE BOTHER!
THAT HAGGIS SUPPER'S AS GOOD AS MINE!
LOOK WHIT YE'VE DONE TAE MY CLEAN WASHIN' YE WEE IMP!
COME ON, APE MAN! THE APE WOMAN'S AFTER YE!
THE VERY DAB! THERE ARE TREES A' THE WAY ALONG HERE!
IT'S EASY, BOAB! COME ON!
HEY! THIS IS MY BRANCH! IT WINNA HAUD US BAITH!
SNAP!
HEY, MISTER! STOP! CRIVVENS, HE CANNAE HEAR US!
FIVE MILES ON—
HERE, WHIT ARE YOU TWA DAEIN' IN THERE?
IT'S A LONG STORY.
AYE, MILES AN' MILES LONG!
WELL, I GOT ACROSS TOON WITHOOT MY FEET TOUCHIN' THE GROUND.
AYE, BUT NOW THEY'RE TOUCHIN' IT TOO MUCH!
THANK GOODNESS I'VE A SPARE BUCKET.

*When it comes to planning fun—*

*Two heads are better than just one!*

HERE, WULLIE, WOULD YOU LIKE THIS OLD DUMMY?
TAILOR
AYE, THANKS.
IT COMES TAE BITS! I'LL HAE SOME FUN WI' THIS!
ER, EXCUSE ME, SIR...
COULD YOU DIRECT ME TO THE HOSPITAL, PLEASE?
HO-HO!
HELP!
HERE'S ANOTHER CHANCE FOR A LAUGH.
LOOK WHIT YE'VE DONE!
HELP! I'VE BURIED HIM IN THE SAND!
HAUD ON, MISTER. I'LL SOON HAE YE OOT!
FOOLED YE, MISTER!
HELP! HELP!
LOOK! HE CANNA SWIM!
HOLD ON. I'M COMING!
OOF!
CHEERIO, MISTER.
AYE-AYE. WHIT'S THIS?
A TAILOR'S DUMMY, EH? NOW I KEN WHIT'S BEEN GOIN' ON.
OH-OH! TIME I WISNAE HERE.
JUST A MINUTE!
HO-HO. THAT'S WHIT YE CA' THE LONG ARM O' THE LAW.
ACH, IT WIS GOOD FUN WHILE IT LASTED.

# *Now Oor Wullie's seeking fame—*

# *As " big boss " in the boxing game!*

HE'S AWA' TAE GET THE AUTOGRAPH O' BATTLIN' BILL, THE BOXER.
BOXING STADIUM
OFFICIALS
HERE THEY COME!
THERE'S BATTLIN' BILL.
OFFICIALS
CRIVVENS! HE'S NO' IN ANY SHAPE TAE SIGN ANY-THIN'!
AND THERE'S SAMMY GOLDMAKER, THE BOXING PROMOTER.
JINGS! AN AMBULANCE FOR BATTLIN' BILL, AN' A POSH CAR FOR THE PROMOTER. I THINK I'LL GET INTAE THE BOXIN' BUSINESS!
MEELORDS, LADEEZ AN' GENULMEN! IN THE BLUE CORNER, FOR SCOTLAND, THE FLEA-WEIGHT CHAMPION O' DRUMTOGLE —SUPER SOUTAR!
AN' HERE COMES THE FUTURE CHAMPION. I'D BETTER GET HIM INTAE TRAININ' STRAIGHT AWAY!
I'VE DECIDED TAE BECOME A BOXIN' PROMOTER, SUPER—ER—SOAPY, AN' YOU'RE TAE BE MY FIRST WORLD CHAMP!
THAT'S FINE BY ME.
I'VE JIST FOUND A SKIPPIN' ROPE, SO YE CAN START TRAININ' WI' THAT.
WHIT ARE YE DAEIN' WI' MY SKIPPIN' ROPE, YE BIG LUMP?
TAK' THAT, AN' I'LL TAK' THIS!
BOP!
OUCH!
GET AWA' WI' YE! YE'LL NO DAE THAT WHEN HE'S WORLD CHAMP!
ANOTHER GUID TRAININ' SCHEME IS TAE RUN WI' HEAVY BOOTS ON.
Wullie's Shed
THESE WELLIES ARE NO' VERY HEAVY, WULLIE.
THEY WILL BE ONCE I'VE FILLED THEM WI' SAND.
ONCE YE'RE FINISHED A' THIS TRAININ', YE'LL MAK' MUHAMMAD ALI LOOK LIKE A FLOWER ARRANGER! RICHT! START RUNNIN'!
AND
ACH, OWER MUCH SAND. NEVER MIND, THAT'LL TOUGHEN UP YER HEID.
OW!
DONG!
COME AN' TRAIN WI' THIS PUNCHBAG INSTEAD.
HELP M'BOAB! A FEATHER-WEIGHT CHAMPION! HA-HA!
HEY, YOU! YE'VE RUINED MY PILLOW, YE SCAMP.
GET OOT O' HERE!
OOYAH!
RIGHT, THAT'S YER TRAININ' FINISHED. RUNNIN' FROM THAT WIFIE HAS BROUGHT YE TAE A PEAK O' PHYSICAL FITNESS.
THERE'S JIST ONE WEE SNAG—I'VE NO' ARRANGED ANY-BODY FOR YE TAE FIGHT.
WELL I KEN SOMEBODY . . .
YOU!
WHACK!
WHIT GRATITUDE! I'LL BET JIM WATT NEVER BELTED HIS BOSS!

*Oor Wullie's got a super plan—*

*To build himself a " cartie-van "!*

HE'S VISITIN' SOAPY.
SEE OOR BRAW MOTOR CARAVAN, WULLIE? WE'VE HIRED IT FOR OOR HOLIDAYS. WE'RE AFF TAE TOUR THE HIGHLANDS.
IT'S GOT SEATS, A COOKER, SINK, FRIDGE, RADIO AN' TV. A' THE COMFORTS O' HAME IN THE MIDDLE OF THE OPEN AIR, AN' BREATH-TAKIN' HIGHLAND SCENERY.
A' THE COMFORTS O' HAME, AN' HIGHLAND SCENERY, EH? I FANCY SOMETHIN' LIKE THAT.
SO—
BANG!
HAMMER!
SAW!
Wullie's Shed.
HOW DAE YE LIKE MY " CARTIE-VAN "?
THERE'S BRAW SCENERY HERE AT LOCH FOWLIE. I'LL STOP HERE THE NICHT.
TIME FOR MY PIECE, NOO . . . HEY, WHIT'S HAPPENIN'? WE'RE MOVIN'!
MICHTY ME! I SHOULD HAVE PUT BRAKES ON IT.
HERE'S A NICE, FLAT, GRASSY BIT. THERE'S NAE WATER ABOOT, EITHER.
BUT—
HELP M'BOAB! THOSE COOS ARE NO' VERY PLEASED WI' ME!
WHEW! JIST MADE IT!
THIS IS MAIR LIKE IT.
NAE SLOPES, NAE LOCHS, NAE COOS—GREAT!
CRIVVENS! I'M SINKIN'! THIS IS A BOG!
HA-HA-HA! THAT'S TREMENDOUS! HOLD IT RIGHT THERE.
HEY! WHIT'S THE BIG IDEA?
THAT'S THE FUNNIEST THING I'VE SEEN IN A LONG TIME.
WHIT A CHEEK! I'VE HAD ENOUGH O' THIS OPEN-AIR BUSINESS.
THIS IS THE LIFE. A' THE COMFORTS O' HAME IN THE MIDDLE O' BRAW HIGHLAND SCENERY.
WE THOUGHT YOU'D GIVEN UP THAT IDEA, WULLIE.
READER'S VOICE
YE'RE RIGHT, BUT THE PHOTOGRAPHER GAVE ME A GREAT BIG PHOTIE O' GLEN BOGLE FOR MAKIN' HIM LAUGH.
IT WIS FAR LESS TROUBLE BRINGIN' THE SCENERY TAE THE HOOSE THAN TAKIN' A HOOSE TAE THE SCENERY.

*It's half-past twelve. " Come on!" Wull cries—*

*And cuts a boaster doon tae size!*

COME HERE A WEE MINUTE, WULLIE.
I'M FED UP O' UNCLE BERT HANGIN' ROOND THE HOOSE EVER SINCE HE CAME TAE VISIT US FROM AMERICA. WHY NO' TAK' HIM OOT, AN' SHOW HIM THE SIGHTS AROOND TOON?
OKAY, MA.
THERE'S SOME BRAW THINGS TAE SEE IN OOR TOON, UNCLE BERT.
Wullie's Hoose.
THIS IS THE POND WHAUR ME AN' MY PALS SAIL OOR BOATS.
CALL THAT A POND? I'VE SEEN BIGGER PUDDLES WHEN MY AUTOMOBILE HAD A LEAKY RADIATOR.
YES, SON, THERE SURE ARE SOME GREAT SIGHTS TO SEE IN THE GOOD OLD U.S.A.
HUH? WHY DID YE NO' JIST STAY THERE, THEN?
THERE'S THE WHINNY BRAES. A GRAND BEAUTY SPOT.
CALL THOSE HILLS? I'VE SEEN BIGGER BUMPS IN MY LAWN BACK HOME IN THE STATES.
EVERYTHING'S SO SMALL HERE IN SCOTLAND. I GUESS YOU ALL JUST THINK SMALL OVER HERE.
HUMPH!
NO' EVERYTHING'S SMALL. THERE'S HEN BROON, THE TALLEST LAD IN TOON.
CALL HIM TALL? BACK IN THE STATES WE'VE GOT MIDGETS BIGGER THAN THAT.
WHIT ABOOT THE BAIRD HALL, THEN? IT'S THE BIGGEST CONCERT HALL FOR MILES.
AW, THAT'S NOTHING. WE'VE GOT BIGGER BUS SHELTERS THAN THAT BACK HOME.
WELL, IT'S HALF PAST TWELVE. I'LL SHOW YE SOMETHIN' NOO— SOMETHIN' YOU YANKS CANNAE BEAT.
HAW! HAW! THIS I MUST SEE!
RIGHT! COME ON, THEN!
WE'RE HOME, MA! IS IT READY YET?
AYE, COME ON IN, WULLIE.
THAT LADDIE O' MINE HAS THE BIGGEST APPETITE IN SCOTLAND. I JIST DINNA KEN WHAUR HE PUTS A' THAT MINCE AN' TATTIES.
GEE! WHAT A PLATEFUL!
MINCE AN' TATTIES— BRAW! UNCLE BERT HAD TAE GIVE UP HALFWAY THROUGH HIS—SO I ATE HIS AN' A'!

*Thanks to Wullie's ploys and pranks—*

*He ends up with TWO piggy banks!*

WELL, PIGGY, IT'S TIME YE WERE OPENED UP.
I'VE SAVED UP FOR LONG ENOUGH. NOO I'M GOIN' OOT TAE SPEND IT A'. I'LL HAVE TAE SMASH YE OPEN WI' A HAMMER, THOUGH, PIGGY.
SHUT YER EYES AN' GET READY, NOO— OOPS! THE HEID'S FLEW AFF!
JINGS! IT'S LANDED IN THAT WIFIE'S HAT!
THANKS FOR STOPPIN' MY HAT, WULLIE. HERE'S TWENTY PENCE.
TA!
THAT WIS LUCKY, BUT I HAVEN'T GOT MY PIGGY BANK OPEN YET.
THE VERY DAB. I'LL STICK IT UNDER THAT ROAD ROLLER.
CAUTION ROAD REPAIRS
OKAY, ALEC, YE CAN KNOCK OFF THERE FOR THE DAY.
ACH!
LOOKS LIKE YE'VE BEEN SAVED AGAIN, PIGGY.
OH, YOU BRAVE BOY! YOU SAVED THAT LITTLE CAT FROM BEING RUN OVER.
EH? WHIT CAT?
DON'T BE MODEST, WILLIAM. I SAW YOU SNATCH IT FROM UNDER THE WHEELS OF THAT THING. HERE, TAKE THIRTY PENCE REWARD.
AYE, B- BUT ...
MRS WILKIE MUST BE GETTIN' AWFY SHORT- SIGHTED.
PARK
WET
HERE'S THE PERFECT SPOT TAE SMASH OPEN MY BANKIE.
BYE- BYE, PIGGY.
CRIVVENS! WHIT'S THAT I'M SITTIN' ON?
MICHTY ME, I NEVER NOTICED THAT 'WET PAINT' SIGN. YE'VE SAVED MY NEW DRESS, SONNY. HERE'S SOMETHIN' TAE YERSEL.
ER, TA!
WET PAINT
I'D HAVE ENDED UP LOOKIN' LIKE A ZEBRA IF I'D SAT THERE.
MAIR LIKE A ZEBRA CROSSING, I'D SAY!
WET PAINT
WELL, I HAVENAE GOT MY BANKIE SMASHED, BUT I'VE MADE LOADS O' MONEY.
CHINK! CHINK!
I THINK I KEN WHIT TAE SPEND IT ON, AN' A!
McKAY
I BOUGHT ANOTHER PIGGY BANK—THEY'RE GREAT FOR MAKIN' MONEY AS WELL AS SAVIN' IT.

*See Soapy chuckle loud and long—*

*When Wullie gets his clues all wrong!*

MY, THAT WIS A BRAW STORY ABOOT SHEERLUCK HOLMES, THE DETECTIVE.

I'VE GOT A' THE RICHT GEAR TAE BE A DETECTIVE.

HA-HA! WHIT ARE YE DRESSED LIKE THAT FOR, WULLIE?

I'M A DETECTIVE. COME ON AN' I'LL AMAZE YE WI' MY POWERS O' DEDUCTION.

SEE A' THESE BONES LYIN' IN THE ROAD? THEY MEAN A TIGER'S ESCAPED FROM THE ZOO.

THE BONES ARE CLOSE TOGETHER, THAT MEANS THAT THE TIGER'S MOVIN' SLOWLY 'COS HE'S STIFF FROM BEIN' CAGED UP . . .

. . . AN' THAT'S HOW I KEN IT'S FROM THE ZOO—CLEVER, EH?

DOG'S HOME

WHIT A NUISANCE. THE DOOR'S SWUNG OPEN AN' A' THESE BONES HAVE FALLEN OOT.

HA-HA! SOME TIGER!

ACH, WELL. EVEN SHEERLUCK HOLMES WIS WRONG SOMETIMES.

AHA! LOOK AT THIS!

GRANPAW BROON HAS JIST WALKED PAST HERE. SEE THE FOOTPRINTS AN' THE MARK O' A WALKIN' STICK ALONGSIDE? YE CAN TELL IT WIS AN AULD MAN BY THE WAY THE STICK'S BEEN PUSHED INTAE THE GROUND WI' HIM LEANIN' HEAVILY ON IT.

WRONG AGAIN, WULLIE. IT'S JIST MRS MARTIN WI' WEE GEORDIE.

AH, WHIT'S THIS, THOUGH?

A HANKIE WI' KNOTS IN IT—THAT MUST BE A MAIDEN IN DISTRESS. IT MUST BE SERIOUS—IT'S WET WI' HER GREETIN'!

I'D BETTER RESCUE HER!

JINGS, YOU'RE NO' A MAIDEN — MAIR LIKE A MIDDEN!

SO THAT'S WHAUR MY HANKIE WENT! I WIS USIN' IT TAE KEEP THE SUN AFF MY HEID WHEN IT BLEW AWA'.

HERE, IT'S A' WET NOW. I THINK IT LANDED IN A DUB.

YE'RE HOPELESS, WULLIE. YE'VE NAE IDEA ABOOT BEIN' A DETECTIVE AT A'.

OH, NO? TAK' A LOOK AT THESE FOOTPRINTS, THEN. THEY WERE MADE BY A SMART ALEC WEARIN' SHORTS . . .

. . . AN' WHIT'S MAIR, HE'S GOT BLACK HAIR AN' HE'S GOIN' TAE GET A KICK IN THE PANTS!

AWA'! HOW CAN YE TELL A' THAT?

'COS YOU MADE THEM WHEN WE WALKED PAST HERE EARLIER ON!

SOAPY WISNAE MUCH GOOD AT DETECTIN' WHIT WIS COMIN' HIS WAY!

*Clean boots, pressed breeks, all spick and span—*

*Now spot Oor Wullie, if you can!*

IS THAT YOU SITTIN' ON THAT BUCKET AGAIN, WULLIE?
JUST LOOK AT YE! YER HANDS ARE BLACK, YER FACE IS FILTHY, YER HAIR'S A MESS, YER DUNGAREES ARE IN TATTERS, AN' YER BOOTS ARE CAKED WI' MUD AGAIN!
AN' WHIT'S MAIR, P.C. MURDOCH TELLS ME YE'VE BEEN PLAYIN' FITBA' IN THE STREET AGAIN!
IF YE GO ON LIKE THIS YE'LL END UP IN THE JAIL!
CRIVVENS! MAYBE THEY'RE RICHT! I'LL HAVE TAE START BEIN GUID AN' BEHAVIN' MASEL'!
SO—
WHA'S THAT SMART WEE LAD COMIN' OOT O' WULLIE'S HOOSE?
MICHTY ME! IT'S WULLIE!
HIYA, WULLIE! COMIN' FOR A GEMME O' FITBA'?
SORRY, ROBERT. FOOTBALL IS A ROUGH, VULGAR SPORT NOT SUITABLE FOR A CHAP LIKE ME.
OOPS! MUSTN'T TOUCH THAT BALL! I'LL GET DIRTY!
HEY, YOU, YE WEE VANDAL!
BUT, SIR, I AM MERELY AN INNOCENT BY-STANDER.
DINNA GIE ME ANY O' YER CHEEK. I'VE SEEN YE KICKIN' THAT BALL ABOOT AFORE!
LATER—
I CAN DO A GOOD DEED HERE AND STOP SOAPY FISHING.
NO FISHING
GIVE ME THAT ROD AT ONCE, YOUNG MAN. IT'S WRONG TO STEAL THE LAIRD'S FISH.
EH?
NO FISHING
OH, ER, OKAY THEN. HERE, TAK' IT.
SO YOU'RE THE LAD THAT'S BEEN PINCHIN' FISH, EH?
NO FISHING
NO, BUT...
STAYING CLEAN AND BEHAVING IS GETTING ME INTO MORE TROUBLE THAN EVER!
Wullie's Hoose.
SURELY WULLIE'S NOT GIVING UP HIS BUCKET FOR A POSH SEAT?
GIE UP MY BUCKET? NEVER!
WELL, I FEEL BETTER FOR THAT. BEIN' GUID IS JIST NO' FOR ME!

Wull's dancing lessons come up trumps—
When he learns ballet jumps!

COME ON, WULLIE, IT'S TIME FOR YER DANCIN' LESSONS.
THIS IS AWFY.
DANCING ACADEMY
SEE AN' ENJOY YERSEL', NOW, WULLIE.
YOU'LL ENJOY THIS, WILLIAM.
SWORD DANCING CLASS
ACH, I DINNA SEE THE POINT O' THIS.
THERE'S THE POINT O' IT!
OW!
I'LL SHOW YOU, SMARTY PANTS!
MAYBE WE SHOULD TRY TAP-DANCING, WILLIAM.
WAIT IN THERE TILL I FETCH YOUR TEACHER.
MOMENTS LATER—
WHAT ON EARTH—?
I CANNA GET THE HANG O' THIS DANCIN' ON THE TAPS.
I DON'T THINK YOU'RE SUITED TO THIS EITHER, WILLIAM. HAVE YOU EVER SEEN MORRIS DANCING?
NO, I DIDNAE EVEN KEN MORRIS COULD DANCE.
OH, DEAR, YOU DON'T HAVE A CLUE, DO YOU?
BALLROOM
WHAT'S YOUR FOOTWORK LIKE AT A BALL?
WELL, MY PALS THINK I'M NO' TOO BAD.
I'LL SHOW YE.
PRETTY GUID, EH?
WHAT A SHOT!
THAT'S NOT WHAT I MEANT AT ALL, WILLIAM!
I DON'T REALLY THINK THERE'S ANY SORT OF DANCING THAT WOULD SUIT YOU, WILLIAM.
WAIT A MINUTE! I RECKON BALLET CLASSES COULD COME IN HANDY!
ER, YES, IF THAT'S WHAT YOU WISH.
WHAT'S THIS? HAS WULLIE GONE SOFT?
NO' LIKELY! WATCH THIS!
A' THAT LEAPIN' WAS BRAW PRACTICE FOR ME REACHIN' UP TAE THESE APPLES!
I SUPPOSE YE'D CALL THIS A "CORE DE BALLET"!

*In the end, oor fly wee buddy—*

*Finds himself the perfect cuddy!*

WHIT A BRAW STORY—A' ABOOT BRONCO BILL, THE COWBOY WHO COULD TAME ANY HORSE.
AH'M AWA' TAE TAME A FEW BUCKIN' BRONCOS.
Wullie's Shed
HANG ON TAE MA HORSE, WULLIE.
SURE THING, PARDNER!
THIS IS TOO EASY— IT'S NO' REALLY A WILD HORSE.
HELP! STOP!
SORRY ABOOT THAT, WULLIE! AULD MRS WILSON AYE GIES HIM SOMETHIN' AN' HE SPOTTED HER DOON THE ROAD.
AH'LL TAME ANE O' THAE TOUGH CRITTERS.
DONKEY RIDES
WHA'S HE KIDDIN'?
OOYAH!
BUCKIN' BRONCOS! THE VERY DAB!
AMUSEMENT ARCADE
NAEBUDY TAE SEE ME. AH'LL TRAIN ON ANE O' THEM.
JINGS! IT'S NO' WORKIN'!
YE'VE TAE KICK THIS ANE TAE MAK' IT WORK.
HELP!
AH'M AWA' HAME.
WULLIE, COULD YE PUT THIS UP FOR ME—THE TUMBLE DRYER'S NO' WORKIN' AGAIN.
JINGS—WHIT A TANGLE!
GIE IT TAE ME!
AH'M NO' MUCH O' A COWBOY. AH CANNAE EVEN TAME A CLOTHES HORSE.
AH KEN WHIT KIND O' BRONCO WID SUIT ME, THOUGH!
Wullie's Shed
HOW DAE YE LIKE MA "BUCKET BRONCO"?

*Wullie does a lot o' frettin'—*

*Until he sees what Murdoch's gettin!*

AH THINK AH'LL HAE A TODDLE ROOND THE TOON.
POLICE
YOU CAN HAVE YOUR CHOICE, MURDOCH — THE NEW BIKE OR THE PANDA.
JINGS, A PANDA CAR OR A BIKE. THIS IS SERIOUS . . .
POLICE
I'LL SOMEHOW HAE TAE PERSUADE HIM TAE TAK' THE BIKE. I CAN OUTRUN HIM ON A BIKE SOMETIMES . . .
ON THE ITHER HAND, IF I JOUKED UP PEESIE'S CLOSE, HE COULD FOLLOW ME ON HIS BIKE.
I'D BETTER PERSUADE HIM TO GO FOR THE PANDA CAR.
BUT IF HE HAD A CAR . . .
. . . JIST THINK O' A THE STUFF HE COULD CONFISCATE!
NAE CRICKET OR FITBA' IN THE STREET!
POLICE
IT'LL HAE TAE BE THE BIKE . . .
HANG ON, THOUGH . . .
IT'S NO' THE FIRST TIME HE'S USED HIS BIKE TAE SEE OWER A FENCE . . .
NO FISHING
IT'S GOT TAE BE THE PANDA CAR.
I'VE JIST REMEMBERED—HE AYE HIDES HIS AULD BIKE AHENT THE SHED WHEN HE NIPS INTO THE BAKERY FOR HIS FLY CUPPIE EVERY MORNING. IT WINNA BE EASY TAE HIDE A CAR.
BAKERY
TWA MORNIN'S WITHOOT HIS CUPPIE, AND HE WIDNAE BE FIT TAE SPEAK TAE!
SO IT'LL JIST HAE TAE BE THE NEW BIKE.
OOYAH!
HELLO, WULLIE, WHIT DAE YE THINK O' THE PANDA I WON FOR MY NEPHEW IN THE POLICE DRAW? I GOT THE CHOICE O' THIS OR A WEE BIKE.
ACH, A' THAT WORRYIN' FOR NOTHIN'!

*Wull's never lonely, never glum—*

*Thanks to his ever-present chum!*

HE'S AWA' PLAYIN' WI' HIS PALS.
SHOOT!
SAVED!
GREAT GEMME, LADS!
WULLIE! JIST LOOK AT YE. FILTHY! NAE TEA FOR YOU, MY LAD. GET UP TAE YOUR ROOM!
AW!
AND YE'RE NO' GETTIN' OOT WI' YER PALS AGAIN.
JINGS! I'M LONELY.
HANG ON, THOUGH . . . I'M NO' ALONE!
PIT UP YER MITTS, PAL!
TAK' THAT!
NOW FOR A GEMME O' HEIDERS!
HEID IT BACK!
SMASHIN'!
YOU'RE NO' BAD!
NOW WE'LL HAE AN OBSTACLE RACE. LET'S SEE WHA CAN REACH THE LIGHT SWITCH FIRST.
READY, STEADY—GO!
HO-HO. A DEAD HEAT!
ACH, MEBBE I'VE BEEN TOO HARD ON THE WEE SOWEL . . .
. . .STUCK UP THERE A' ON HIS OWN.
COME ON. OOT YE COME, WULLIE. YE MUST BE LONELY . . .
LONELY? NO' ME. I'VE BEEN PLAYIN' WI' MY PAL!
YE'RE A GREAT WEE CHUM!

*Oor Wullie's quick with words, and how—*

*His big fat chum is FLAT Bob now!*

HIYA, FOLKS!
HI, WULLIE. WE'RE JIST WATCHIN' RAB GILLESPIE PENTIN' HIS HOOSE.
IT'S GREY— NO' A VERY BRIGHT COLOUR.
CRASH!
HE'S A' GREY!
AYE—WE'LL HAE TAE CALL HIM 'DRAB' GILLESPIE NOO!
THAT WIZ AWFY QUICK O' YE, WULLIE!
AYE—AH'M A SMART LAD, YE KEN.
OOYAH!
SORRY, SONNY! CANNAE STOP—GOT AN APPOINTMENT AT THE SLIMMING CLUB.
AYE, IF YE CAN GET IN!
THAT WIZ A CLOSE THING. WE MIGHT HAE HAD TAE CALL YE 'FLAT' BOB!
DID YE KEN THAT THE FIRST SIGN O' BEIN' STUPID IS HAIRS ON THE PALMS O' YER HANDS?
NO, AH DIDNAE.
AN' THE SECOND SIGN IS LOOKIN' FOR THEM!
WE'LL HAE TAE CALL YOU 'DOPEY' SOUTAR FRAE NOO ON!
YOU'RE AWFY CLEVER!
AYE—AH KEN!
HMM! THAE STONES LOOK SLIPPERY!
AFTER YOU.
AARGH!
SLIP!
WE'LL HAVE TAE CA' YE WEET ECK NOW!
THAT DOES IT! WE'RE TIRED O' YER SMART IDEAS!
HANG ON. I WIS JIST JOKIN'. COME ON, I'LL TREAT YE TAE SOME SWEETIES.
WHAT'LL WE BUY? TAILS IT'S GRANNY SOOKERS, HEIDS IT'S SOOR PLOOMS.
HELP! THERE GOES MY MONEY—DOON THE DRAIN.
NOW THEY'RE CALLIN' ME POOR WULLIE!

*Four times Murdoch's hat's sent flyin'—*

*And Wullie isn't even tryin'!*

I'LL HAE SOME FUN WI' THAE CANS.
NOW TAE KNOCK THEM DOON!
HOI!
YE WEE RASCAL!
JINGS, IT WIZ AN ACCIDENT!
PHEW! I'VE GIVIN' HIM THE SLIP!
HARDWARE
AH, WULLIE— WILL YE DAE ME A FAVOUR?
TAKE THIS NEW BROOM TO MRS WILKIE. HERE'S 10P TO YOURSELF!
I'D BE A BRAW DRUM MAJOR.
CRIVVENS! I'VE DONE IT AGAIN!
I'D BETTER TAK' THE LANG WAY ROOND TAE MRS WILKIE'S!
MUCH LATER—
THAT'S THE BROOM DELIVERED. NOW I'LL HAE TAE KEEP A LOOK-OUT FOR MURDOCH!
NAE SIGN O' MURDOCH ROOND HERE. HMM, THAT'S A HANDY PIECE O' ROPE.
I'LL LASSO THAT FENCE POST!
OH, NO— NO' AGAIN!
I'LL GET YE FOR THIS, WULLIE!
PHEW! I'VE SHAKEN HIM AFF!
HI, WULLIE— KICK THE BA' BACK!
HERE'S MA CANNONBALL SPECIAL!
JINGS! THAT HAT'S HAUNTING ME!
SCRAM!
IT'S TIME I SNEAKED HAME!
PHEW! HERE AT LAST!
Wullie's hoose
BUT—
AH, WULLIE—P.C. MURDOCH WANTS A WORD WI' YE!
HELP! HE GOT HERE FIRST!
HE SAID HE'D LET ME AFF, IF I GAVE HIM A CHANCE TAE GET HIS AIN BACK!

*It's the funniest thing yet—*

*When he tracks doon this pet!*

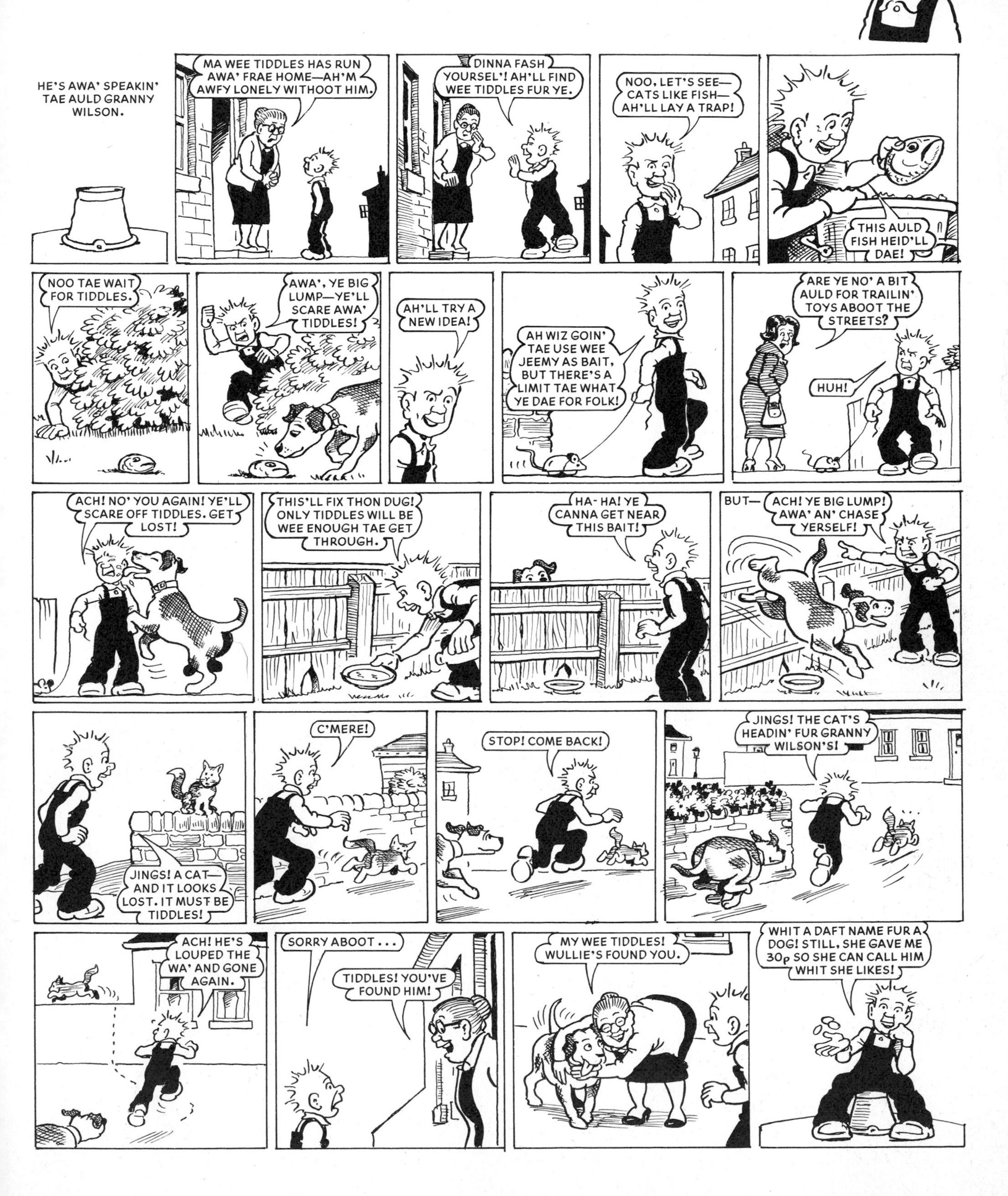
HE'S AWA' SPEAKIN' TAE AULD GRANNY WILSON.
MA WEE TIDDLES HAS RUN AWA' FRAE HOME—AH'M AWFY LONELY WITHOOT HIM.
DINNA FASH YOURSEL'! AH'LL FIND WEE TIDDLES FUR YE.
NOO, LET'S SEE—CATS LIKE FISH—AH'LL LAY A TRAP!
THIS AULD FISH HEID'LL DAE!
NOO TAE WAIT FOR TIDDLES.
AWA', YE BIG LUMP—YE'LL SCARE AWA' TIDDLES!
AH'LL TRY A NEW IDEA!
AH WIZ GOIN' TAE USE WEE JEEMY AS BAIT, BUT THERE'S A LIMIT TAE WHAT YE DAE FOR FOLK!
ARE YE NO' A BIT AULD FOR TRAILIN' TOYS ABOOT THE STREETS?
HUH!
ACH! NO' YOU AGAIN! YE'LL SCARE OFF TIDDLES. GET LOST!
THIS'LL FIX THON DUG! ONLY TIDDLES WILL BE WEE ENOUGH TAE GET THROUGH.
HA-HA! YE CANNA GET NEAR THIS BAIT!
BUT—
ACH! YE BIG LUMP! AWA' AN' CHASE YERSELF!
JINGS! A CAT—AND IT LOOKS LOST. IT MUST BE TIDDLES!
C'MERE!
STOP! COME BACK!
JINGS! THE CAT'S HEADIN' FUR GRANNY WILSON'S!
ACH! HE'S LOUPED THE WA' AND GONE AGAIN.
SORRY ABOOT . . .
TIDDLES! YOU'VE FOUND HIM!
MY WEE TIDDLES! WULLIE'S FOUND YOU.
WHIT A DAFT NAME FUR A DOG! STILL, SHE GAVE ME 30p SO SHE CAN CALL HIM WHIT SHE LIKES!

*See the scarf that Wullie's got—*

*And then see how it keeps him hot!*

HE'S NO' OUT YET.
IT'S FREEZIN' CAULD OOTSIDE. PIT ON THE SCARF AUNTY AGGIE KNITTED FOR YE!
BUT MAW . . . IT'S TOO BIG . . . AND FANCY . . . AND BESIDES, I DINNA LIKE WEARIN' A SCARF.
AWA' YE GO. AND NAE ARGUIN'!
HUH!
ROVER—STOP PULLING!
SNAP!
ITS LEAD'S SNAPPED!
GOT YE!
THANKS, WULLIE!
CRIVVENS, PUFF—PANT—HE'S NO' HALF POWERFUL!
JINGS, THERE'S WEE SAMMY . . .
CLOSED
FASTER! FASTER!
PANT!
TA-TA!
PHEW! THAT WIZ HARD WORK!
WHAT'S THAT?
OH, ER, JUST AN AULD SCARF.
IT MAK'S A RARE TUG-O'-WAR ROPE!
HEAVE!
PUFF—PANT!
PUFF!
LOOK OUT!
YEOWPS!
RUN FOR IT! PUFF! PANT!
IT'S NO' SO COLD NOW, WULLIE. YOU CAN TAK' THAT SCARF AFF NOW.
YOU'RE JOKIN'! I GET TOO HOT EVERY TIME I TAK' IT AFF!

# *When everything is said and done—*

# *No one's a "patch" on Wull for fun!*

ONCE YE'VE BEEN TAE MRS WILKIE'S JUST COME STRAIGHT HOME. YE SHOULD HAE ENOUGH MONEY.
Wullie's Hoose
AYE, DINNA WORRY.
JINGS! HERE'S MR DONALDSON!
I'LL BE A'RICHT IN HERE!
HELLO, WILLIAM.
ER.. HELLO MR DONALDSON.
PHEW! THAT WIS CLOSE!
LOOKS LIKE THE COAST'S CLEAR, NOW!
CRIVVENS! IT'S BOAB AN' SOAPY!
BETTER TAK' COVER DOON HERE.
CAUTION MEN AT WORK
HI, LADS!
HEY, THERE'S WULLIE.
WHIT'S HE DAEIN' DOON THERE?
IT MUST BE ANE O' HIS TRICKS! COME ON, SOAPY!
GET OOT O' THERE, YE WEE DEVIL!
A'RICHT, A'RICHT, I'M GOIN'!
OH, NO! HERE COMES AULD MURDOCH! WHIT CAN I DAE?
GOT TAE THINK FAST...
WHIT'S THIS THEN, A SIT DOON PROTEST?
NAW, IT'S JIST A SIT DOON!
I THOUGHT I COULD UNDERSTAND YOUNG FOWK NOWADAYS— NOW I'M NO' SAE SURE!
M. WILKIE.
DRAPER'S
HERE AT LAST!
HI, WULLIE! WANT A LIFT?
THANKS, MR SMALL. I'M JIST ON MY WAY HAME!
THANKS FOR THE LIFT! CHEERIO!
'BYE, WULLIE.
HERE YE ARE, MA. LET'S GET IT OVER WI'!
I'LL PUT ON THE PROPER PATCH YE GOT FROM MRS WILKIE STRAIGHT AWAY.
WHIT A RELIEF! I COULDNAE BEAR TAE BE SEEN WI' THAT THING ON MY BREEKS!
YE WINNA TELL BOAB OR SOAPY, WILL YE?

*Some smart replies—*

*Then a big surprise!*

HE'S AWAY TO SCHOOL.
DID YE HEAR TAM SPALDING'S TAE BE JOININ' THE POLIS, WULLIE?
I DIDNA KEN THE POLIS WERE COMIN' APART!
I'VE GOT A' THE ANSWERS. TALKIN' O' THE POLIS, DID I TELL YE ABOUT THE CHEEK I GAVE OLD MURDOCH?
I MUST ASK YOU TO ACCOMPANY ME TO THE STATION, YOUNG MAN!
WHY? DON'T YE KNOW THE WAY BY YERSEL'?
I'M NO' SCARED O' ANYBODY! TAK' THE OTHER DAY WHEN I WIS FISHIN' UP AT DUNCRAIG LOCH . . .
YOU CAN ONLY CATCH FISH HERE WITH A PERMIT!
OCH, AWA'! I'M CATCHIN' PLENTY WI' WORMS!
YOU'RE RIGHT, WULLIE. YOU'VE GOT A' THE ANSWERS.
AYE! TUFTY CRAIG WIS SHOWIN' AFF HIS DOG TAE ME YESTERDAY . . .
SCHOOL
YE'D BETTER NO' PAT MY DOG, OR HE'LL SNAP!
I DIDNA THINK DOGS WERE THAT EASILY BROKEN!
LOOK AT A' THIS MESS! I WISH YOU LOT WID USE THE LITTER BINS!
BUT WE DO . . .
SCHOOL
. . . THEY MAK' BRAW GOALPOSTS!
CHEEKY MONKEY!
WE HAD A BRAW LAUGH IN THE MATHS CLASS YESTERDAY . . .
THIS IS QUITE A DIFFICULT CALCULATION, SO WATCH THE BLACKBOARD WHILE I RUN THROUGH IT . . .
I WIDNA DAE THAT, SIR . . .
. . . YE MIGHT HURT YERSEL' RUNNIN' THROUGH THE BLACKBOARD!
HA-HA! I'VE GOT ANSWERS FOR A' THING!
RIGHT, CLASS! TAKE OUT THE ANSWERS TO LAST NIGHT'S HOMEWORK EXERCISE!
JINGS! I'VE FORGOTTEN MINE!
TAKE 100 HUNDRED LINES, WILLIAM! THAT SHOULD TEACH YOU TO REMEMBER YOUR HOMEWORK!
HEE-HEE! PITY YE DIDNA HAE A' THE ANSWERS THERE, EH, WULLIE?
WULLIE'S SPEECHLESS—FOR ONCE!

*Things don't go quite as Wullie planned—*

*So see how his Pa " lends a hand "!*

I'VE BEEN GETTIN' INTAE TROUBLE LATELY. I MUST TRY AN' DAE SOMETHIN' USEFUL.
I'LL BE A HANDYMAN.
THE FIRST JOB I'LL DAE IS . . .
OOYAH!
THE FIRST JOB IS TAE FIX THE TOOLBOX!
NOW I'M A' SET!
THERE'S A JOB I COULD DAE. MR YEOMAN NEEDS A NEW 'Y' FOR HIS SIGN.
EOMAN
NEWSAGENT
SHORTLY—
THERE! THAT DIDNA TAK' LANG!
SO, MAKIN' A NEW CATTIE, EH? I TOLD YE YE WEREN'T TAE PLAY WI' THESE DANGEROUS THINGS!
BUT, PA . . .
HE NEVER GAVE ME A CHANCE TAE EXPLAIN. I'LL GET BACK IN HIS GUID BOOKS AGAIN, THOUGH.
THIS AULD GATE'S BEEN STICKIN' FOR YEARS. FIXIN' THIS IS NAE PROBLEM FOR A HANDYMAN LIKE ME.
LATER—
PEAT
JINGS! WHIT A WEIGHT THESE SACKS ARE! BETTER GIE THE GATE A GUID DUNT!
YIKES!
PEAT
PEAT
ER . . . DID YE NOTICE I'D FIXED THE GATE, PA?
PEAT
HMM . . . LOOK AT THAT NAIL STICKIN' OOT. BETTER FIX THAT, TOO. SOMEONE COULD CATCH HIS JERSEY ON IT.
GRUNT! PECH! IT'S A LONG ANE!
GOT IT!
WULLIE! LOOK WHIT YE'VE DONE, NOW!
I DIDNA KEN THAT NAIL WIS HOLDIN' THE SHED TOGETHER!
I WIS ONLY TRYIN' TAE BE A HANDYMAN, PA.
REALLY? WELL, NOW IT'S MY TURN . . .
. . . TAE BE A HANDY MAN!

*Oor Wullie may be good at " chessies "—*

*But he's a flop at writing essays!*

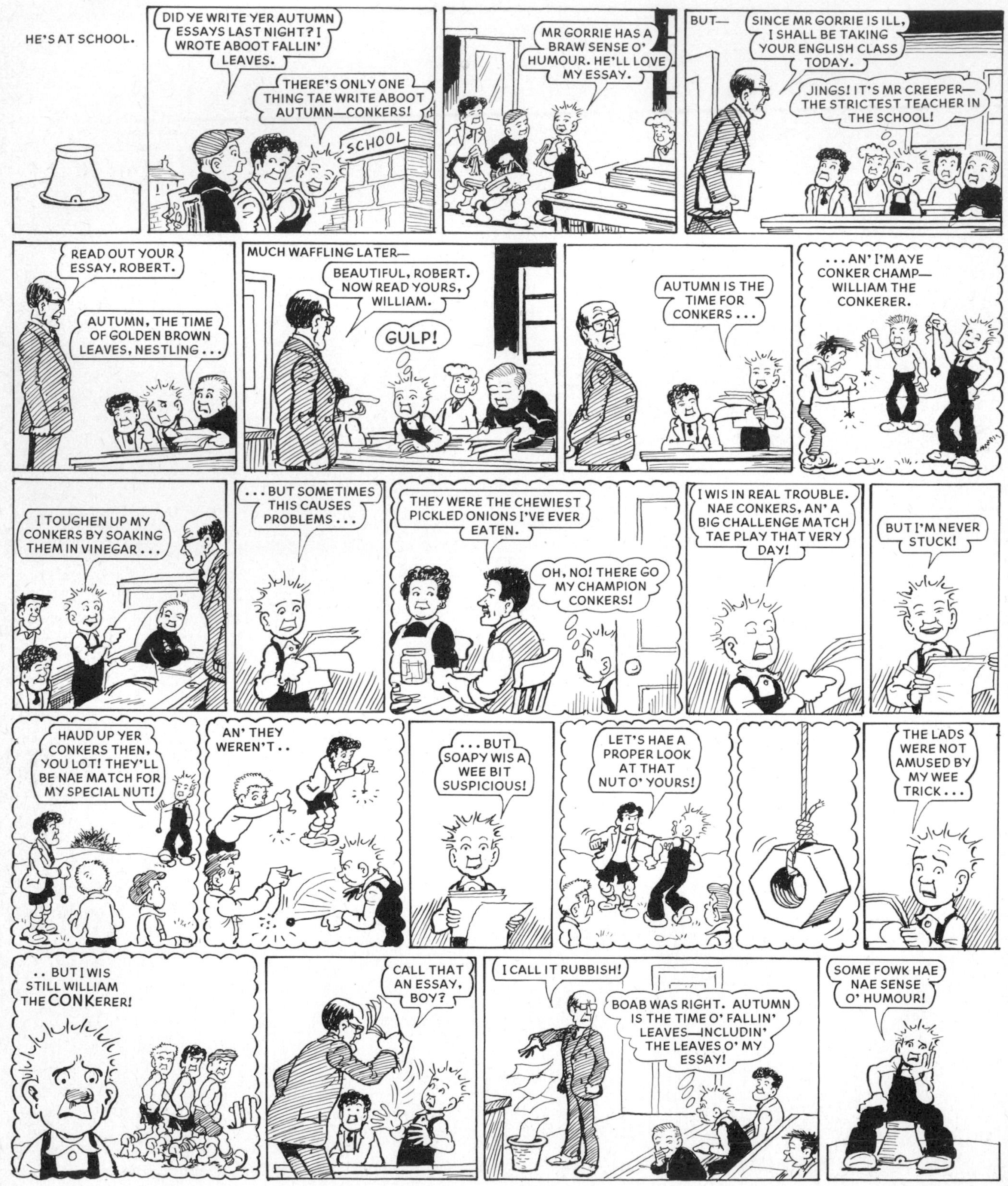

HE'S AT SCHOOL.
DID YE WRITE YER AUTUMN ESSAYS LAST NIGHT? I WROTE ABOOT FALLIN' LEAVES.
THERE'S ONLY ONE THING TAE WRITE ABOOT AUTUMN—CONKERS!
SCHOOL
MR GORRIE HAS A BRAW SENSE O' HUMOUR. HE'LL LOVE MY ESSAY.
BUT—
SINCE MR GORRIE IS ILL, I SHALL BE TAKING YOUR ENGLISH CLASS TODAY.
JINGS! IT'S MR CREEPER—THE STRICTEST TEACHER IN THE SCHOOL!
READ OUT YOUR ESSAY, ROBERT.
AUTUMN, THE TIME OF GOLDEN BROWN LEAVES, NESTLING . . .
MUCH WAFFLING LATER—
BEAUTIFUL, ROBERT. NOW READ YOURS, WILLIAM.
GULP!
AUTUMN IS THE TIME FOR CONKERS . . .
. . . AN' I'M AYE CONKER CHAMP—WILLIAM THE CONKERER.
I TOUGHEN UP MY CONKERS BY SOAKING THEM IN VINEGAR . . .
. . . BUT SOMETIMES THIS CAUSES PROBLEMS . . .
THEY WERE THE CHEWIEST PICKLED ONIONS I'VE EVER EATEN.
OH, NO! THERE GO MY CHAMPION CONKERS!
I WIS IN REAL TROUBLE. NAE CONKERS, AN' A BIG CHALLENGE MATCH TAE PLAY THAT VERY DAY!
BUT I'M NEVER STUCK!
HAUD UP YER CONKERS THEN, YOU LOT! THEY'LL BE NAE MATCH FOR MY SPECIAL NUT!
AN' THEY WEREN'T . .
. . . BUT SOAPY WIS A WEE BIT SUSPICIOUS!
LET'S HAE A PROPER LOOK AT THAT NUT O' YOURS!
THE LADS WERE NOT AMUSED BY MY WEE TRICK . . .
. . BUT I WIS STILL WILLIAM THE CONKERER!
CALL THAT AN ESSAY, BOY?
I CALL IT RUBBISH!
BOAB WAS RIGHT. AUTUMN IS THE TIME O' FALLIN' LEAVES—INCLUDIN' THE LEAVES O' MY ESSAY!
SOME FOWK HAE NAE SENSE O' HUMOUR!

Cups of every shape and size—

But will Wull EVER win a prize?

LOOK, WULLIE! I WON THIS AT AN ATHLETICS MEETING!
MY, THAT'S BRAW, SAMMY!
WONDER IF I'LL EVER WIN A CUP?
I COULD ALWAYS ENTER JEEMY IN A "MOOSE OBEDIENCE" CONTEST.
STAY!
BUT THEY WID GIE THE CUP TAE JEEMY!
PROUD!
THERE'S AYE OOR FITBA' TEAM TAE THINK ABOOT, I SUPPOSE.
WE MIGHT WIN THE DRUMDARROCH CUP THIS YEAR . . .
. . . BUT I KEN WHA'D HAE TAE LOOK AFTER IT!
IF I HAD A GUID PARTNER, I MICHT WIN A TROPHY AT TENNIS DOUBLES NEXT YEAR . . .
THANK YOU, I'LL TAK' IT.
NO, I WILL!
I SAID I'D TAK' IT!
NO, I . . . OOPS!
I WONDER IF THERE'S A TROPHY FOR CARTIE RACIN'?
I'VE AYE BUILT THE FASTEST CARTIES IN TOON . . .
BUT I AYE FORGET TAE FIT BRAKES!
WULLIE'S GOT THE CUP!
AYE, AN' WE'LL NEED THE FIRE BRIGADE TAE GET IT AFF HIM!
I DINNA SUPPOSE I'LL EVER GET A CUP.
AH, WULLIE! YE'RE JUST IN TIME . . .
. . . FOR A CUP O' TEA!
HA-HA! I GOT A CUP AFTER A'!
THAT'S MY KIND O' CUP—TO A 'T'!

# A box o' chalks—

# Brings Wullie shocks!

I HEAR THERE'S A NEW LAD COMIN' TAE STAY ROOND HERE. I'LL HAVE TAE GO AN' MEET HIM.
HIYA, WULLIE!
HI, LADS!
THIS IS ALEC SMART. HE'S JIST MOVED IN TAE GOWRIE STREET.
HELLO. I'M WULLIE, AN' I'M THE HEID LAD AROOND HERE 'COS I'M THE CLEVEREST ANE!
HEY, WULLIE, HAVE YE SEEN THE MAN ROOND THE CORNER HOLDIN' UP A BUS WI' ONE HAND?
THIS I MUST SEE!
WELL, WULLIE, THERE HE IS.
ACH!
LOOK! THERE'S TEN PENCE!
IT'S MINE! I SAW IT FIRST!
EH?
HA-HA! I'VE GOT IT ON A THREAD! FOOLED YE AGAIN!
COULD YE NO' SEE THE THREAD? TIME YE HAD YER EYES CHECKED!
HAVE YOUR EYES EVER BEEN CHECKED?
NO . . .
. . . THEY'VE ALWAYS BEEN PLAIN BROWN!
HUMPH! I'M NO' STAYIN' HERE TAE BE LAUGHED AT!
ACH, DINNA GO AWA' IN THE HUFF, WULLIE. HERE'S A PRESENT FOR YE. YE CAN HAE MY BOX O' CHALKS.
JINGS! MAYBE ALEC'S NO' SUCH A BAD LAD AFTER A'!
SO! I MICHT HAVE GUESSED IT WIS YOU!
WHIT?
DON'T DENY IT! I'VE CAUGHT YE RED-HANDED WI' THOSE CHALKS!
I'LL GET MY OWN BACK ON THAT ALEC!
P.C. MURDOCH, TWA FLAT FEET, HEID LIKE A PUDDIN' AN' A FACE TAE MAKE YE GREET.
LATER—
SO YE THINK YE CAN DRAW, EH, ALEC?
AYE, I CAN DRAW ANYTHIN'.
FINE! IF I CAN PROVE YE WRANG YE CAN BUY US A' FISH SUPPERS OOT O' TONI'S.
NAE TROUBLE. THERE'S NOTHIN' I CAN'T DRAW.
GRANNY WILSON CAN DRAW SOMETHIN' YOU CANNA! JIST YOU WATCH!
POST OFFICE
THERE! SHE'S GOIN' IN TAE DRAW HER AULD AGE PENSION!
I'LL HAE A HELPIN' O' PEAS WI' MINE!
BROON SAUCE FOR ME!
HA-HA! I'M THE HEID LAD AGAIN!

*All Wullie's hopes go sadly wrong—*

*Some queues are best when they are long!*

HE'S AWA' TAE THE PICTURES.
NEMA
I'M FAIR LOOKIN' FORWARD TAE SEEIN' TWA GUN TONY.
HEY, ECK! YE'LL HAVE TAE JOIN THE QUEUE IF YE WANT IN!
NO' ME! MY COUSIN'S THE DOORMAN! I'LL GET IN NAE BOTHER!
CINEMA
IN YE GO, ECK.
THANKS, SAM.
ACH, IT'S FULL UP, NOW!
HOUSE FULL
I'LL AWA' AN' GET MASEL' A FISH SUPPER INSTEAD.
HOUSE FULL
FISH SUPPERS
JINGS! NO' ANOTHER QUEUE!
YE COULD DIE O' STARVATION WAITIN' IN THAT QUEUE, WULLIE! NO' ME, THOUGH. MY COUSIN WORKS HERE.
FISH SHO
TWA HELPIN'S O' CHIPS WI' MY BLACK PUDDIN' PLEASE, JOCK.
ANYTHIN' YE SAY, BOAB.
FISH SUPPERS
SEE YE, WULLIE.
HUH! HE SKIPPED IN FRONT O' A'BODY!
I'M FED UP O' NO' BEIN' FED UP. I'M AWA' HAME.
MICHTY! ANOTHER WAIT!
BUS STOP
ROOM FOR THE FIRST TWA ONLY!
OH, NO! NOW I'LL HAVE TAE WALK HAME!
COME ON, SOAPY! THERE'S ROOM FOR YOU!
GREAT! IT'S BRAW HAVIN' A COUSIN WHO'S A BUS DRIVER!
WHIT A LIFE! A' MY PALS HAVE GOT COUSINS TAE SEE THEM TAE THE FRONT O' QUEUES.
HOME AT LAST—
COME AN' MEET YER COUSIN TONY, WULLIE. YE'LL BE REAL PROUD O' HIM WHEN YE HEAR WHAT HE DOES!
GREAT! MAYBE HE'S A CIRCUS RINGMASTER!
OR HE COULD BE ON THE TURNSTILES AT THE FITBA'!
THIS IS TONY, WULLIE. HE'S JUST QUALIFIED AS A DENTIST!
JINGS! THAT'S JIST THE SORT O' QUEUE YE DINNA WANT TAE BE IN FRONT O'!
DENTIST
WHIT A DAY! I STARTED OOT WI' TWA GUN TONY, AN' ENDED UP WI' TWA GUM TONY!

*You'll no' half goggle when you look—*

*At the title o' Wull's library book!*

I'D BETTER TAK' MY LIBRARY BOOK BACK
THERE IT IS ON THE SHELF.
WULLIE! I TOLD YE NO' TAE COME IN HERE! I'VE JIST VARNISHED THE FLOOR!
SORRY, PAW. I FORGOT!
STICK!
IT'S MILES TAE THE LIBRARY. I'LL GET THE BUS.
HEY! WHIT ARE YE PLAYIN' AT? WHY DID YE NO' STOP?
THE BUS DOESNAE STOP THERE ANY MAIR, SONNY. THEY MOVED THAT STOP ROOND INTAE SCOTT STREET LAST MONTH.
OH, ER, AYE . . . IT SLIPPED MY MIND.
I'LL WALK ROOND BY MRS WILKIE'S SHOP AN' BUY SOME SWEETIES.
E. PATERSON. HIGH CLASS HAIR SALON
HELP M'BOAB! I FORGOT A' ABOOT MRS WILKIE SELLIN' HER SHOP TAE THON HAIRDRESSER!
THERE'S BOB AN' SOAPY. HULLO, YOU TWA. WHAUR DID YE GET THAE BALLOONS?
DID YE NO' MIND ABOOT THON NEW TOY SHOP OPENIN' THE DAY? THEY WERE GIVIN' BALLOONS AWA'!
SHOE REPAIRS.
HOW CAN I FORGET A' THESE THINGS?
HEY, WULLIE! WHEN ARE YE COMIN' TAE COLLECT YER BOOTS? THEY'VE BEEN READY FOR MONTHS!
OH, ER . . . I'LL BE IN THE MORN—IF I REMEMBER!
I'LL TAK' A SHORT CUT THROUGH HERE.
JINGS! I FORGOT THEY'D DUG A' THIS STREET UP!
CLOSED UNTIL FURTHER NOTICE.
HUH! HOPE I CAN MIND WHAUR THE LIBRARY IS, NOO!
HERE AT LAST!
HUMPH! TUT-TUT! THIS BOOK IS TWO WEEKS LATE, YOUNG MAN!
AYE, I'M AFRAID I FORGOT TAE BRING IT BACK.
HA-HA-HA! THAT'S A LAUGH! DON'T YOU REMEMBER WHAT IT'S CALLED, EITHER?
HOW TO HAVE A GOOD MEMORY.
IT'S NO' FUNNY! I FORGOT TAE READ IT AN' A'!

*Oor lad's a Scot, we can't deny it—*

*He's even on a haggis diet!*

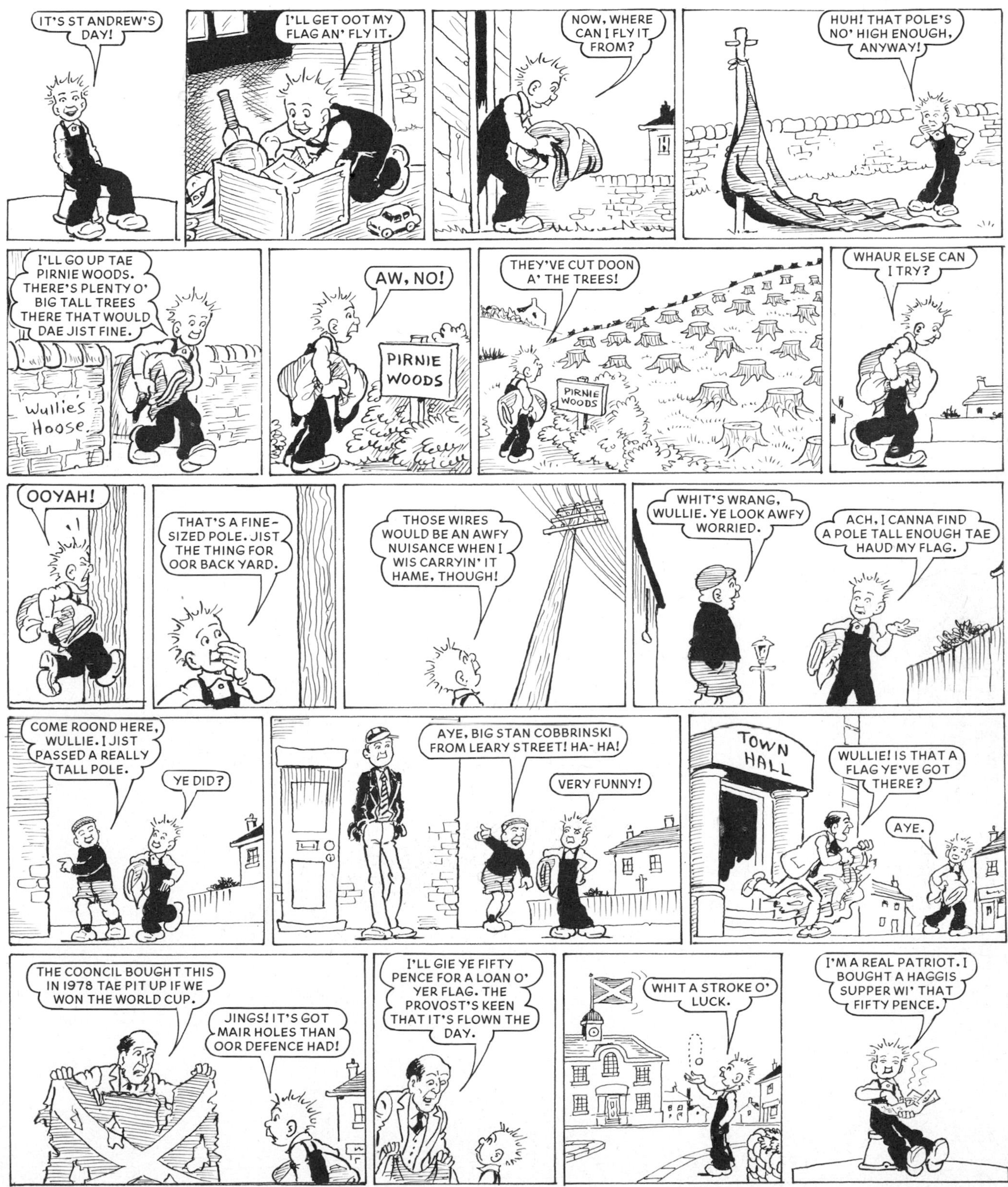

IT'S ST ANDREW'S DAY!
I'LL GET OOT MY FLAG AN' FLY IT.
NOW, WHERE CAN I FLY IT FROM?
HUH! THAT POLE'S NO' HIGH ENOUGH, ANYWAY!
I'LL GO UP TAE PIRNIE WOODS. THERE'S PLENTY O' BIG TALL TREES THERE THAT WOULD DAE JIST FINE.
Wullie's Hoose
AW, NO!
PIRNIE WOODS
THEY'VE CUT DOON A' THE TREES!
PIRNIE WOODS
WHAUR ELSE CAN I TRY?
OOYAH!
THAT'S A FINE-SIZED POLE. JIST THE THING FOR OOR BACK YARD.
THOSE WIRES WOULD BE AN AWFY NUISANCE WHEN I WIS CARRYIN' IT HAME, THOUGH!
WHIT'S WRANG, WULLIE. YE LOOK AWFY WORRIED.
ACH, I CANNA FIND A POLE TALL ENOUGH TAE HAUD MY FLAG.
COME ROOND HERE, WULLIE. I JIST PASSED A REALLY TALL POLE.
YE DID?
AYE, BIG STAN COBBRINSKI FROM LEARY STREET! HA-HA!
VERY FUNNY!
TOWN HALL
WULLIE! IS THAT A FLAG YE'VE GOT THERE?
AYE.
THE COUNCIL BOUGHT THIS IN 1978 TAE PIT UP IF WE WON THE WORLD CUP.
JINGS! IT'S GOT MAIR HOLES THAN OOR DEFENCE HAD!
I'LL GIE YE FIFTY PENCE FOR A LOAN O' YER FLAG. THE PROVOST'S KEEN THAT IT'S FLOWN THE DAY.
WHIT A STROKE O' LUCK.
I'M A REAL PATRIOT. I BOUGHT A HAGGIS SUPPER WI' THAT FIFTY PENCE.

*Poor Oor Wullie comes off worst—*

*When the lads' new ba' is burst!*

COME ON, WULLIE. LET'S TRY OOT THE FITBA' WE SAVED UP TAE BUY!
A'RICHT!
HA-HA! YE'LL NO' TAK' THE BA' AFF ME, SOAPY.
TOO SLOW FOR AN ACE LIKE ME, BOAB!
ACH, I MADE A MESS O' THAT SHOT, THOUGH!
OOPS! THAT'S THE BA' SCUNNERED!
LOOK WHIT YE'VE DONE! YE'LL BUY US ANOTHER BA'—OR ELSE!
SPORTS
I'LL TRY IN HERE. FITBA'S ARE EXPENSIVE, THOUGH.
I'D LIKE A FITBA', PLEASE. I CAN GIE YE TEN PENCE NOW, AN' TEN PENCE A WEEK FROM NOW ON.
CHEEKY MONKEY!
SPORTS SHOP
OOT YE GO!
HA-HA! HE DIDNA GET A BA', BUT HE GOT THE BOOT!
HEY, WULLIE! THERE'S TWA MEN ROOND HERE THROWIN' OOT A BALL!
GREAT!
ROOM
BALL
THAT'S IT, LADS. TAK' THAT SIGN DOON, IT'S A BINGO IN HERE, NOO!
BINGO
OH, VERY FUNNY!
WHIT ARE YE SO GLUM ABOOT, WULLIE?
ACH, I'VE NAE FITBA' AND I CANNAE AFFORD TAE BUY ANE.
NEVER MIND. I'VE SOME AULD SPORTS STUFF IN MY SHED. IT'S A' YOURS, IF YE'LL DIG MY GARDEN!
IT'S A DEAL!
HUH! THANKS FOR THE HELP!
YOU BURST THE BA', YOU GET US ANOTHER ANE!
MUCH LATER—
HEY! THIS IS A' THERE WAS IN THE SHED!
AYE, I DIDNA SAY ANYTHIN' ABOOT A FITBA'!
ACH, MY BA'S IN THOSE NETTLES. I'LL NEVER GET IT OUT.
GOLF CLUB
DINNA WORRY. I'M JIST THE LAD YE'RE LOOKIN' FOR!
WI' A' THIS GEAR ON, I CAN GET BALLS BACK NAE BOTHER!
LOOK AT THIS! THERE'S DOZENS O' BALLS IN HERE!
CLUB HOUSE
HA-HA! I'M MAKIN' A FORTUNE!
GOLF BALLS 20P
GOAL! THAT NEW BA'S A BEAUTY!
YE CANNA SAY I'M NO' ON THE BALL!

*Eck's got a moothie, there's a fiddle and a drum—*

*And the orchestra leader's your funny wee chum!*

HE'S AWA' TAE A CONCERT WI' HIS UNCLE JIM.
IS THIS WHAUR WE HEAR SOME FUNNY ORCHESTRA, UNCLE JIM?
NO' ' SOME FUNNY ORCHESTRA '—A SYMPHONY ORCHESTRA.
THEY'RE PLAYIN' BEETHOVEN'S UNFINISHED SYMPHONY IN C MINOR, WULLIE.
HA-HA! THAT MUST BE ' C ' FOR COAL—COAL ' MINOR '!
THIS IS BRAW!
THAT WIS GREAT, UNCLE JIM! I THINK I'LL START MY AIN ORCHESTRA.
NEXT DAY—
RIGHT, LADS, WE'LL START OFF WI' A SELECTION O' CHICK OVSKY'S LATEST HITS.
WAIL!
SCREECH!
THUMP!
WHIT'S A' THIS DIN? YE'VE WOKEN MY BAIRN!
SORRY, MISSUS! RUN FOR IT, LADS!
LET'S GO DOON TAE TONI'S CHIPPER. I'VE GOT A GREAT IDEA.
YE'LL HAE A HIGH CLASS ORCHESTRA SERENADIN' YER CUSTOMERS.
A'RIGHT, WULLIE, I GIVE YOU A TRY.
HOWL!
TWA PUDDEN SUPPERS AN'A SINGLE FISH!
WHAT'S THAT YOU SAY? I NO' HEAR YOU RIGHT.
ACH, NEVER MIND! YE CANNA HEAR YERSEL THINK WI' THAT RACKET GOIN' ON!
BLARE!
SORRY, BOYS. ORCHESTRAS IS NO' GOOD FOR BUSINESS. YOU GO NOW, PLEASE.
ACH, OKAY, TONI.
I KEN! WE CAN PRACTISE IN THE AULD BANDSTAND IN THE PARK!
WOOOYEEOOOOEEEEE
THAT'S IT, BOAB! YE'RE FAIR GETTIN' THE HANG O' THON FIDDLE!
EXCUSE ME, LADS. I HEARD YE PLAYIN', AN' I WORK FOR THE COONCIL. I'D LIKE YE TAE PLAY AT THE BAIRD HALL THE NIGHT.
GREAT!
THIS IS OOR BIG CHANCE! WE COULD GO RIGHT TAE THE TOP!
STAGE
AYE, YE'LL CERTAINLY GO RIGHT TAE THE TOP!
JIST PLAY UP ON THE ROOF FOR AN HOUR OR SO TAE STOP A' THESE STARLINGS FROM ROOSTIN'HERE!
WE CAN AYE SAY WE HAD AN AUDIENCE O' THOOSANDS!

*There's a real how-d'ye-do—*

*At Wullie's wee zoo!*

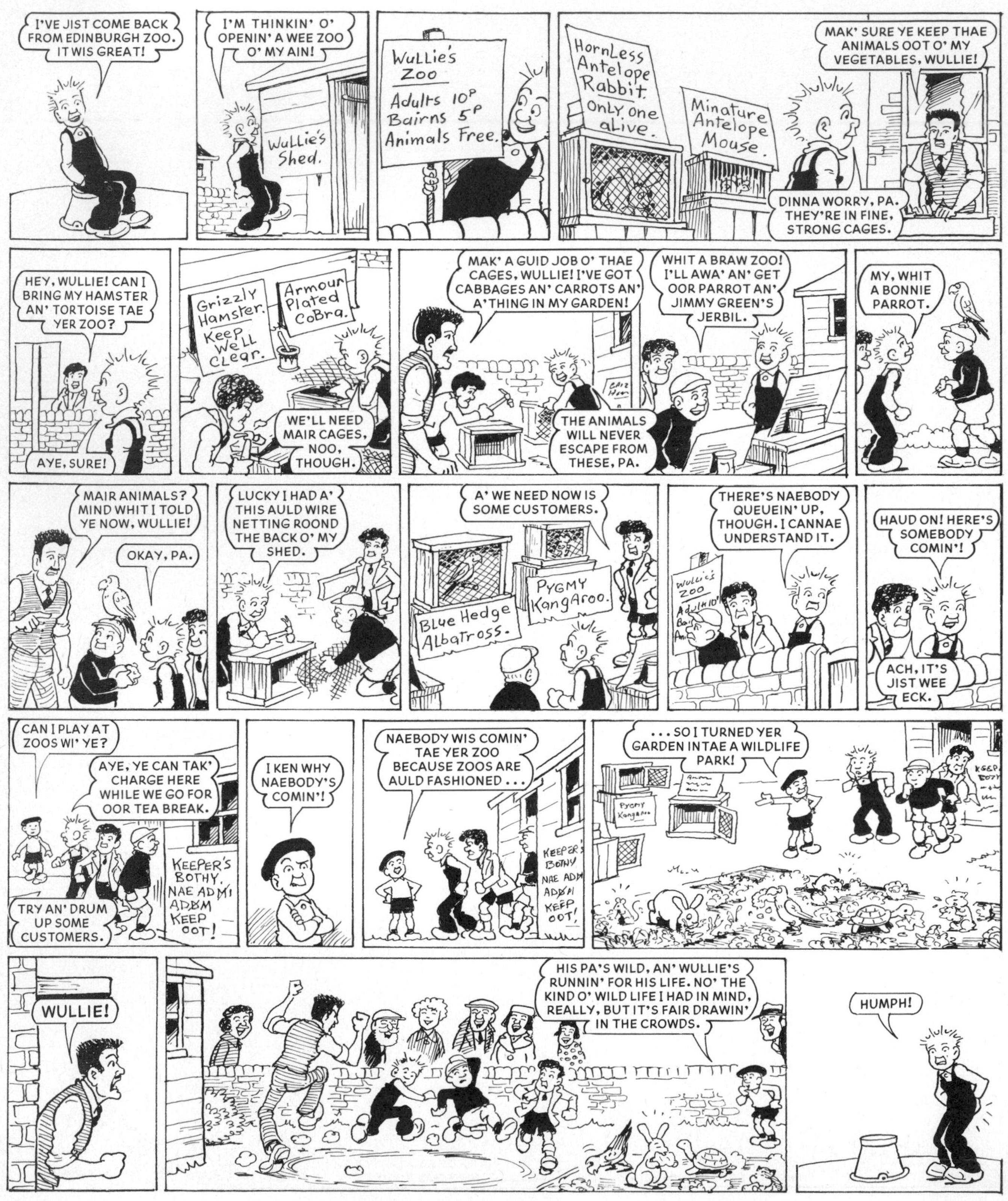

I'VE JIST COME BACK FROM EDINBURGH ZOO. IT WIS GREAT!
I'M THINKIN' O' OPENIN' A WEE ZOO O' MY AIN!
Wullie's Shed.
Wullie's Zoo
Adults 10P
Bairns 5P
Animals Free.
Hornless Antelope Rabbit. Only one alive.
Minature Antelope Mouse.
MAK' SURE YE KEEP THAE ANIMALS OOT O' MY VEGETABLES, WULLIE!
DINNA WORRY, PA. THEY'RE IN FINE, STRONG CAGES.
HEY, WULLIE! CAN I BRING MY HAMSTER AN' TORTOISE TAE YER ZOO?
AYE, SURE!
Grizzly Hamster. Keep Well Clear.
Armour Plated CoBra.
WE'LL NEED MAIR CAGES, NOO, THOUGH.
MAK' A GUID JOB O' THAE CAGES, WULLIE! I'VE GOT CABBAGES AN' CARROTS AN' A'THING IN MY GARDEN!
WHIT A BRAW ZOO! I'LL AWA' AN' GET OOR PARROT AN' JIMMY GREEN'S JERBIL.
THE ANIMALS WILL NEVER ESCAPE FROM THESE, PA.
MY, WHIT A BONNIE PARROT.
MAIR ANIMALS? MIND WHIT I TOLD YE NOW, WULLIE!
OKAY, PA.
LUCKY I HAD A' THIS AULD WIRE NETTING ROOND THE BACK O' MY SHED.
A' WE NEED NOW IS SOME CUSTOMERS.
Blue Hedge Albatross.
PYGMY KangAroo.
THERE'S NAEBODY QUEUEIN' UP, THOUGH. I CANNAE UNDERSTAND IT.
HAUD ON! HERE'S SOMEBODY COMIN'!
ACH, IT'S JIST WEE ECK.
CAN I PLAY AT ZOOS WI' YE?
AYE, YE CAN TAK' CHARGE HERE WHILE WE GO FOR OOR TEA BREAK.
TRY AN' DRUM UP SOME CUSTOMERS.
KEEPER'S BOTHY. NAE ADMI ADDM KEEP OOT!
I KEN WHY NAEBODY'S COMIN'!
NAEBODY WIS COMIN' TAE YER ZOO BECAUSE ZOOS ARE AULD FASHIONED . . .
KEEPER'S BOTHY NAE ADM ADM KEEP OOT!
. . . SO I TURNED YER GARDEN INTAE A WILDLIFE PARK!
WULLIE!
HIS PA'S WILD, AN' WULLIE'S RUNNIN' FOR HIS LIFE. NO' THE KIND O' WILD LIFE I HAD IN MIND, REALLY, BUT IT'S FAIR DRAWIN' IN THE CROWDS.
HUMPH!

*See the look on this 'tec's face—*

*When he helps Murdoch " crack a case "!*

THAT WIS A BRAW PROGRAMME. SHERLOCK ROCKFALL'S THE BEST DETECTIVE ON TELLY.
THE END
I COULD BE AN ACE DETECTIVE AN' A'!
HERE'S MY AULD MAGNIFYIN' GLASS. A' THE BEST DETECTIVES USE THESE.
THAT HAT'S JIST THE JOB FOR A DETECTIVE AN' A'!
WULLIE!!
THREE O' MY FRESH-BAKED DOUGHNUTS ARE MISSIN'! WHAUR ARE THEY?
I SEE . . .
. . . AND WHEN DID YOU LAST SEE THEM, MADAM? CAN YOU GIVE ME A DESCRIPTION?
WELL, THEY'RE SORT O' ROOND WI' . . . NEVER MIND THAT! WHAUR ARE THEY?
AHA! THESE CRUMBS ARE A VALUABLE CLUE!
HMM . . . THE TRAIL ENDS RIGHT HERE.
BEHOLD! THE CULPRIT!
PA!
GULP!
HA-HA! I GOT A REWARD FOR SOLVIN' MY FIRST CASE!
LATER—
THERE'S P.C. MURDOCH. HE MUST BE WORKIN' UNDER COVER THE DAY.
ARE YE WORKIN' ON A BIG CASE, P.C. MURDOCH?
IT'S CERTAINLY A BIG CASE, WULLIE.
NEED ANY HELP?
AYE, I'LL NEED A' THE HELP I CAN GET.
HAVE YE CRACKED IT YET?
AYE, AN' I'M ABOOT TAE LIFT THE LID AFF THE WHOLE THING.
HAUD ON—THIS COULD GET DANGEROUS!
ER . . . YE'LL NO' BE NEEDIN' YER TRUNCHEON, WILL YE?
A TRUNCHEON WID BE NAE USE ON THIS CASE, WULLIE. IT'S A CROW-BAR I'LL BE NEEDIN'!
RIGHT, WULLIE. WE'LL GO IN ROOND THE BACK.
BUT THIS IS YER AIN HOOSE!
P.C. MURDOCH
AYE, MY NEW BARROW WIS DELIVERED THE DAY, BUT I COULDNA GET THE LID AFF THIS PACKIN' CASE!
I TOLD HIM A' ABOOT IT AFTER. HE HAD A GUID LAUGH AN GAVE ME TEN PENCE FOR HELPIN' HIM.

*Though Tiny Terrors be their name—*

*They're mighty big lads, just the same!*

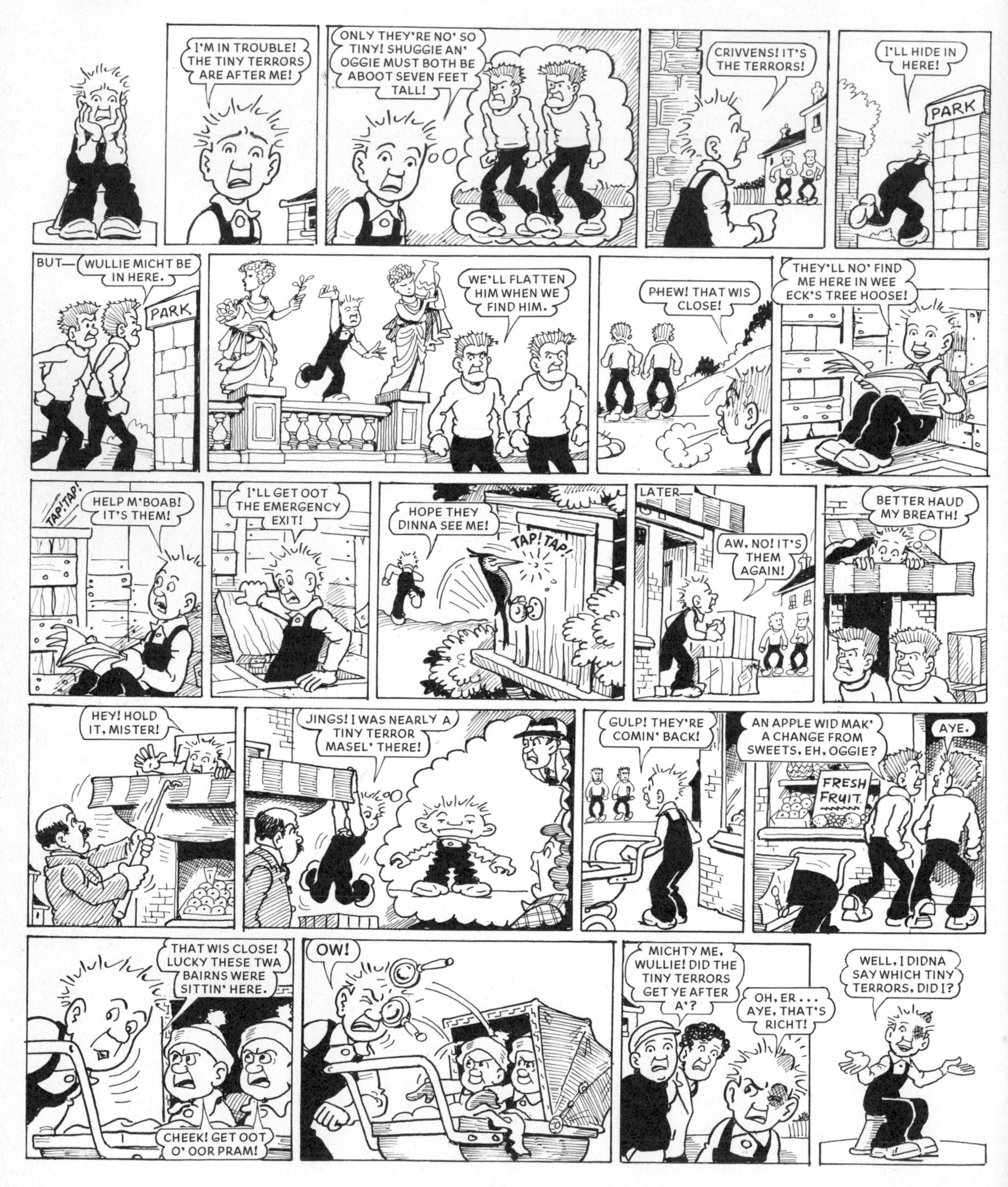

I'M IN TROUBLE! THE TINY TERRORS ARE AFTER ME!
ONLY THEY'RE NO' SO TINY! SHUGGIE AN' OGGIE MUST BOTH BE ABOOT SEVEN FEET TALL!
CRIVVENS! IT'S THE TERRORS!
I'LL HIDE IN HERE!
PARK
BUT—
WULLIE MICHT BE IN HERE.
PARK
WE'LL FLATTEN HIM WHEN WE FIND HIM.
PHEW! THAT WIS CLOSE!
THEY'LL NO' FIND ME HERE IN WEE ECK'S TREE HOOSE!
TAP! TAP!
HELP M'BOAB! IT'S THEM!
I'LL GET OOT THE EMERGENCY EXIT!
HOPE THEY DINNA SEE ME!
TAP! TAP!
LATER—
AW, NO! IT'S THEM AGAIN!
BETTER HAUD MY BREATH!
HEY! HOLD IT, MISTER!
JINGS! I WAS NEARLY A TINY TERROR MASEL' THERE!
GULP! THEY'RE COMIN' BACK!
AN APPLE WID MAK' A CHANGE FROM SWEETS, EH, OGGIE?
AYE.
FRESH FRUIT
THAT WIS CLOSE! LUCKY THESE TWA BAIRNS WERE SITTIN' HERE.
CHEEK! GET OOT O' OOR PRAM!
OW!
MICHTY ME, WULLIE! DID THE TINY TERRORS GET YE AFTER A'?
OH, ER... AYE, THAT'S RICHT!
WELL, I DIDNA SAY WHICH TINY TERRORS, DID I?

*He disna half get up tae capers—*

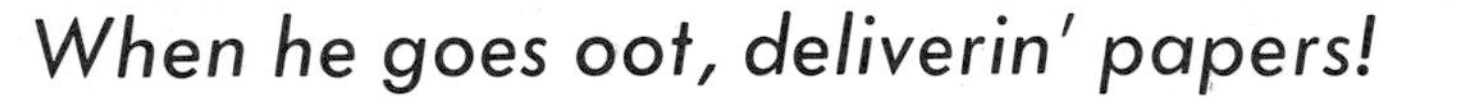
When he goes oot, deliverin' papers!

THIS IS THE DAY I START MY PAPER ROUND.
OFF YE GO, THEN, WULLIE.
CHEERIO, MR WILSON. I'LL BE FINISHED IN NO TIME.
JIST THIS LAST ONE FOR NUMBER FIFTY-EIGHT, THEN I'M DONE!
MY, WHIT A BIG DOG! ER . . . NICE DOGGIE!
GRRR!
WOWF!
HELP M'BOAB! THAT WIS A NEAR THING!
I'LL CREEP OOT ALONG THON BRANCH, AN' SHOVE THE PAPER IN THE DOOR.
THE BRANCH IS BENDING! GULP! MAYBE THIS WISNAE SUCH A GUID IDEA!
WOOF!
ANOTHER FOOT OR TWA AN' THON BEAST WOULD'VE HAD ME FOR BREAKFAST!
NOW THERE'S A BETTER IDEA. CAN I BORROW ANE O' YER PIPES, PLEASE?
SURE, WULLIE.
THIS IS JIST THE JOB.
WI' THIS PIPE, I CAN STICK THE PAPER RIGHT IN THE DOOR.
BONK!
OOPS!
HEY! WATCH WHIT YE'RE DAEIN', OR I'LL CHARGE YE WI' ER . . . RECKLESS SOMETHIN' OR OTHER!
HERE, LOOK AT THAT! WHY DID I NO' THINK O' THAT BEFORE?
SNARL!
I CAN PUT THE PAPER IN THROUGH THE WINDIE!
WOBBLE!
I CANNA QUITE REACH. I'LL . . . OH, NO! I'M GOIN' TAE FA'!
I'VE HAD IT, NOO! THON DOG'S A KILLER!
HERE, WHIT ARE YE DAEIN' IN MY BONNY BUSH?
NEVER MIND! CALL AFF YER DOG AFORE IT EATS ME ALIVE!
OH, ROVER'S QUITE FRIENDLY, REALLY, BUT HE ALWAYS LIKES TO CARRY THE PAPER INTAE THE HOUSE. DID MR WILSON NO' TELL YE ABOOT THAT?
HAPPY!
I'M TAKIN' UP DELIVERIN' MILK INSTEAD. A' THE DOGS ARE STILL ASLEEP THAT EARLY IN THE MORNIN'!

*Just see the perils Wullie meets—*

*As he goes struggling doon the streets!*

ARE YE COMIN' FOR A GEMME O' FITBA', WULLIE?
NO' THE DAY, LADS. I'VE GOT TAE GO HAME AN' MEET MY COUSIN ANGUS FROM CANADA.
SCHOOL
I'M NO' LOOKIN' FORWARD TAE THIS. ANGUS IS AN AWFY BIG-HEID. HE'S ALWAYS BRAGGIN'.
STILL, BETTER NO' BE LATE. I'LL TAK' A SHORT CUT UP THIS LANE.
JINGS! COUGH! UGH!
SORRY, WULLIE!
WHIT A MESS! I COULD HAVE SUFFOCATED IN A' THAT DUST!
SOME FOWK JIST DINNA WATCH WHIT THEY'RE DAEIN'!
WATCH OOT, WULLIE!
YEUGH!
SORRY, WULLIE, BUT YE WALKED RIGHT INTAE IT.
ACH, WELL, AT LEAST IT'S WASHED A' THE DUST AFF.
CRIVVENS! IT'S THE DAWSON ROAD GANG!
WOO! WOO! WOO!
SCALPUM PALEFACE!
I'LL NIP OWER HERE. THEY'LL NO' FOLLOW ME THIS WAY.
OOF!
WHIT ARE YE DAEIN' WI' MY CLOTHES HORSE, YE WEE DEVIL?
HELP M'BOAB! IT'S WITCHIE WILSON!
THAT WIS CLOSE! SOAPY SAYS SHE TURNS YE INTAE A FROG IF SHE CATCHES YE IN HER GARDEN!
HERE'S WULLIE NOW—LATE AS USUAL!
WHY ARE YE ALWAYS LATE? YER COUSIN ANGUS IS NEVER LATE HAME, AN' HE'S BEEN TELLIN' ME HE HAS TAE COME HAME FROM SCHOOL THROUGH BLIZZARDS AN' A' THING!
BLIZZARDS? HUH! THAT'S NOTHIN'!
ON MY WAY HAME FROM SCHOOL I CAME THROUGH A DUST STORM AN' A MONSOON! THEN I WIS CHASED BY SCREAMIN' RED INDIANS, ATTACKED BY A HORSE, AN' I ONLY JIST MANAGED TAE ESCAPE FROM AN ANGRY AULD WITCH!
I WID BE THANKFUL IF A WEE BLIZZARD OR TWA WIS ALL I HAD TAE WORRY ABOOT.
HA-HA! THAT PIT THEIR GAS AT A PEEP, EH?

*On history, Wull's really keen—*

*Till he comes to the battle scene!*

HE'S AWA' ON A HISTORY TOUR.
. . . AND HERE, LADIES AND GENTS, ARE THE OLD STOCKS . . .
PLEASE WALK THIS WAY.
WELL, I'M DAEIN' MY BEST.
HA-HA!
OBSERVE THE CANNONBALL HOLE IN THE WALL.
I THINK I'LL CONDUCT MY AIN GUIDED HISTORY TOUR.
I'LL HAVE TAE MAK' SOME BIG NOTICES FIRST.
NO' BAD, EH?
OOR WULLIE'S GUIDED HISTORIC TOUR. SEE THE ANCIENT RELICS. TUPPENCE PER PERSON OR TEN JEELY BABIES.
EVERYONE FOR THE GUIDED TOUR WALK THIS WAY.
YE'RE KIDDIN'! MY LEGS CANNAE DAE THAT!
OBSERVE THE UPPER JAWBONE OF THE EXTINCT SABRE-TOOTHED WALRUS . . .
LOOKS LIKE A SET O' FALSERS TAE ME.
UPPER JAWBONE OF THE EXTINCT SABRE-TOOTHED WALRUS.
MAKIN' FUN O' MY TEESH! I'LL SHUMP YER LUGSH IF I CASH YE!
HERE WE HAVE SOME WONDERFULLY WELL-PRESERVED FOOTPRINTS OF THE PREHISTORIC DINOSAURUS MURDOCKUS, NOW EXTINCT.
FOOTPRINT OF THE EXTINCT PREHISTORIC DINOSAURUS MURDOCKUS
RUMBLE! THUNDER!
GULP! ARE YE SURE IT'S EXTINCT, WULLIE?
PREHISTORIC? EXTINCT? ROAR!!
FOOTPRINTS OF THE EXTINCT PREHISTORIC DINOSAURUS MURDOCKUS
BAKER ALFRED & Co.
AN' THIS IS ANE OF THE ORIGINAL CAKES BURNT BY ALFRED IN FOURTEEN OATCAKE . . .
GET AWA' WI' YE! I'LL HAVE YE KNOW THAT CAKE WAS BAKED THIS MORNIN'—AN' IT'S NO' BURNT!
WELL, LADS, WHIT DID YE THINK O' THE TOUR?
THERE WAS ONE SIGN YE DIDNAE PUT UP. THE ANE ABOOT THE BATTLE.
BATTLE? WHIT BATTLE?
THIS BATTLE! GRAB HIM, LADS!
THAT'S OOR MONEY BACK.
AYE, WHIT A SWINDLER, EH?
ACH, WELL, IT WIS A LAUGH WHILE IT LASTED!

# Wull's cowboy talk—

## Gives Ma a shock!

HE'S PLAYIN' IN THE HOOSE.
GEE UP, HOSS! THEM INJUNS IS CATCHIN' UP!
WHIT DAE YE THINK YE'RE DAEIN'! GET AFF O' THERE THIS MINUTE!
JINGS! BIG SQUAW SURE AM MIGHTY ANGRY!
THE CROOKED SHERIFF WIS AFTER THE LONE STRANGER.
THERE WIS NAE COVER IN THE DESERT EXCEPT FOR A CLUMP O' CACTUS!
WULLIE! GET OOT O' MY RHUBARB! YE'LL RUIN IT!
THE SHERIFF CHASED THE LONE STRANGER OOT O' THE CACTUS. NOW THERE WIS ONLY ONE WAY TAE SAVE HIMSEL'—HEAD FOR THE HILLS!
SHOWIN' HIS AMAZIN' SKILL, THE LONE STRANGER SCALED A SHEER CLIFF FACE NAE BOTHER!
AN' WIS THEN FACED BY A SAVAGE MOUNTAIN LION!
BUT THE LONE STRANGER WIS ALSO A CHAMPION WRESTLER . . .
DOGGONE!
EH?
NO, CAT GONE!
WHIT DAE YE MEAN BY FRIGHTENIN' MY WEE ERIC, YE BIG LOUT?
I'VE BEEN WATCHIN' YE, WULLIE! A' THIS COWBOY NONSENSE IS CAUSIN' NOTHIN' BUT TROUBLE!
I DINNA WANT TAE HEAR ANY MAIR COWBOY TALK FROM YOU! IT'S TIME TAE HANG UP YER GUNS!
THERE'S AULD GRANNY MURCHIE. SHE LOOKS LIKE SHE COULD DAE WI' A HELP.
HELP ME, WULLIE? SURE YE CAN! YE CAN CLEAN UP MY AULD COOKIN' RANGE FOR A START!
I'LL DAE MY BEST!
TWO HOURS LATER—
MY, WHIT A BRAW JOB YE'VE MADE. I'VE GOT TEN PENCE HERE FOR YE.
BACK HOME—
WULLIE, HOW DID YE GET IN SUCH A MESS?
I WIS WORKIN' ON GRANNY MURCHIE'S RANGE.
WHIT DID I TELL YE ABOUT A' THON COWBOY TALK?
CHEEKY MONKEY!
NO, YE DINNA UNDERSTAND . . .
HA-HA! THEY SAW THE FUNNY SIDE IN THE END. IMAGINE GRANNY MURCHIE AS A COWBOY, THOUGH! HA-HA!

Sandy's super swimming gear—

Comes in really handy here!

HE'S AWA' TAE THE BATHS.
HI, SANDY. I'M AFF TAE THE BATHS.
SO AM I.
WE'LL GET THE BUS JIST ROOND THE CORNER HERE.
JINGS! WE'LL GET OOR FEET WET GOIN' THROUGH A' THAT.
BUS STOP
CAUTION BURST WATER MAIN
I'LL NO'! I'VE GOT MY FLIPPERS WI' ME.
ACH, I'M SOAKIN' ALREADY!
MY FLIPPERS FAIR KEPT OOT THE WATER.
I'M DROOKIT!
BUS STOP
BUS STOP
THERE SHOULD BE A BUS SOON.
JINGS! THAT WIFIE'S ONIONS ARE MAKIN' MY EYES WATER!
THEY WINNA BOTHER ME! I'VE GOT MY GOGGLES.
HUH!
AH, HERE'S THE BUS AT LAST.
BUS STOP
CRIVVENS! IT'S AWFY SMOKY IN HERE!
I'VE GOT JIST THE THING FOR THIS.
GREAT, EH?
OH, AYE! COUGH! BRAW, SANDY! SPLUTTER!
I CANNA WAIT TAE GET IN THE WATER!
BATHS
SORRY, BOYS, YOU'LL HAVE TO HANG ON UNTIL I FIND MY SPECS. I'VE LOST THEM IN THE DARK UNDER THE COUNTER.
HERE, BORROW MY FROGMAN'S UNDERWATER TORCH.
THANKS, SONNY! YOU CAN GO IN FOR FREE!
PAY
BUT YOU'LL HAVE TO PAY!
AND SO—
I'VE BEEN LOOKIN' FORWARD TAE THIS A' DAY!
CHANGING ROOMS
MAIN POOL THIS WAY.
HEY, SANDY! WHAUR ARE YE GOIN'? THE POOL'S THIS WAY.
I KEN, WULLIE, BUT I'M GOIN' IN HERE. I CANNA SWIM, YE SEE!
PADDLING POOL.
WELL, YE MUST ADMIT, SANDY'S THE BEST EQUIPPED PADDLER IN SCOTLAND!

*Things are lookin' up this summer—*

*Oor Wullie's goin' tae be a " plummer "!*

THINK I'LL HAE A WALK DOON THE TOON!
MY, THON'S A BRAW STATUE. I WONDER WHA IT IS?
THAT'S SIR ERNIE TENNERS, WULLIE. HE GAVE MONEY FOR THE LIBRARY AND SWIMMIN' BATHS. HE WAS ALWAYS HELPIN' FOWK!
MAYBE I'LL HAE A STATUE ONE DAY IF I HELP A'BODY.
LOOK AT THAE PLANKS. I'LL SHIFT THEM AFORE SOME PUIR SOUL TRIPS OWER THEM.
THIS'LL BE A GREAT HELP.
THAT'S A GUID JOB DONE.
AAH!
YE WEE HOOLIGAN! YE UNCOVERED THON WORKHOLE!
I WIZ JUST TRYIN' TAE HELP!
THON AULD RAG'S BLOWN OWER SOMETHIN'. I'LL TAK' IT AWA'.
HEY, YOU! PUT THAT BACK, YOU LITTLE SCRUFF! THE LORD PROVOST'S ABOUT TO UNVEIL THAT NEW DRINKING FOUNTAIN!
JINGS! I'M NO' BEIN' MUCH HELP AT A'!
I CANNA GO WRANG IF I SHOVEL A' THIS COAL DOON THON COAL HOLE!
WHEW! HARD WORK THIS!
STILL, THAT'S IT FINISHED NOW. I'VE BEEN A BIG HELP TAE SOMEBODY.
HERE! WHIT HAVE YOU BEEN UP TAE?
JIST SHOVELLIN' COAL, MISTER!
WHIT? IT TOOK ME TWA DAYS TAE SHOVEL THON COAL OOT O' THE CELLAR! I'M MOVIN' HOOSE AN' TAKIN' THE COAL WI' ME!
OOPS! WRANG AGAIN!
HA-HA! THAT'S THE BEST LAUGH I'VE HAD IN AGES! FANCY YOU FLINGIN' A' MISER METHVEN'S COAL BACK DOON THE CELLAR.
WELL, I WIS TRYIN' TAE HELP, REALLY.
I'VE BEEN HELPIN' FOWK A' DAY, BUT SOMETHIN' AYE GOES WRANG.
NEVER MIND. I KEN SOMEBODY YE CAN HELP.
HERE. HELP YERSEL'! TAK' AS MANY PLUMS AS YE LIKE. YE CERTAINLY HELPED CHEER ME UP THE DAY!
JINGS!
I'VE GIVEN UP BEIN' A HELPER AN' DECIDED TAE BECOME A 'PLUMMER'!

*See wee Wullie's latest ploy—*

*A garage owner, that's oor boy!*

THINK I'LL AWA' FOR A WALK.
MY, THAT'S A BRAW HOOSE. I WONDER WHA LIVES THERE?
ADMIRIN' THAT BIG HOOSE, WULLIE? THAT'S WHAUR GEORGE MACMUNY, THE GARAGE OWNER STAYS. YE COULD SAY THAT CARS BUILT THAT HOOSE.
STARTIN' UP MY AIN GARAGE BUSINESS MICHT NO' BE SUCH A BAD IDEA, YE KEN!
THAT'S HANDY—A PILE O' WOOD. I'LL MAK' SOME CARTIES AN' SELL THEM.
LATER—
I'LL NEED SOME WHEELS, NOO.
THESE AULD PRAM WHEELS SHOULD DAE JIST FINE.
DUMP.
WULLIE'S GARAGE.
HIGH CLASS CARTIES
EASY TERMS!
NOO WE'RE IN BUSINESS!
GOOD DAY, SIR. WID YE LIKE TAE TRY OOR DE LUXE SPORTS MODEL?
IT'S NO' VERY DE LUXE. THERE'S NO' EVEN A RADIO.
SO—
THIS'LL DAE.
DUMP.
HUMPH! BOB'S GONE.
I'M LOOKIN' FOR AN ESTATE CAR WI' A HEATER.
CRIVVENS! CAN NONE O' MY CUSTOMERS TAK' THE CARTIES AS THEY ARE?
THIS'LL MAK' A GUID HEATER.
DUMP.
ECK DIDNA WAIT LANG, EITHER. THERE'S NAE SIGN O' HIM.
HAVE YOU GOT A CARTIE WITH A VANITY MIRROR, WILLIAM?
WAIT RICHT HERE, PRIMROSE. I'LL GET YE ANE.
JIST THE JOB.
DUMP.
ANOTHER IMPATIENT CUSTOMER! THEY EXPECT ME TAE DAE A'THING YESTERDAY.
WHAUR'S A' THE WOOD THAT WIS IN THE GARDEN EARLIER ON? IT'S FOR MY NEW SHED.
AW, NO! BANG GOES A' MY SHOWROOM STOCK.
YE'LL GET WOOD SOMEWHERE ELSE, WULLIE. DINNA BE DOON IN THE DUMPS.
DOON IN THE DUMPS? I'VE BEEN DOON IN THE DUMPS A' DAY GETTIN' STUFF FOR MY CUSTOMERS!
ACH, WELL, I SUPPOSE YE COULD SAY THAT CARTIES BUILT THAT SHED.

*Some folk think gardening keeps you fit—*

*But Wull can't see the " point " of it!*

COULD YE DAE A WEE JOB FUR ME?
MA HUSBAND FORGOT THIS—HE'S ENTERED IT FUR THE FLOOER SHOW AT THE TOON HALL. YE'LL SEE HIM DOON THERE.
AYE, OKAY.
THIS IS AN EASY JOB!
JINGS!
BANG!
BUT—BUT—IT WISNAE MA FAULT.
YE WEE VANDAL!
PHEW! BETTER KEEP RUNNIN'!
HOI!
RIP!!
CRIVVENS! TWA WIFIES NOW!
I'LL NIP ROOND HERE, OOT O' SIGHT!
NOW, NO' A SOUND . . .
THAT'S DONE IT!
OOYAH!
THEY'RE A' ON TAE ME AGAIN!
HEY! COME BACK WI' MY CANDY FLOSS!
THE TOON HALL AT LAST!
HERE YE ARE, MR MACPHERSON—YE FORGOT TAE BRING THIS.
THANKS, WULLIE. HERE'S 10P TAE YE—EH?
I'M GETTIN' OOT O' HERE!
OOT O' PUFF, EH? UP TAE NAE GOOD, AH'LL BET! WHY CAN YE NO' TAK' UP A NICE QUIET HOBBY LIKE THAE GAIRDENERS IN THE TOON HA'?
HUH!
AH THINK AH'LL TAK' UP ALL-IN WRESTLIN'—IT'LL BE A REST FROM PLANTS!

*See a bully come a cropper—*

*When it comes to hat-tricks, Wullie's a " topper "!*

HELLO, MR ROBERTSON. WHIT'S THAT YE'RE CHUCKIN' OOT?
ACH, IT'S JIST A LOAD O' AULD HATS, WULLIE.
STAGE DOOR
THEY'RE BRAW! MIND IF I TAK' THEM?
HAE THEM IF YE WANT, WULLIE. THEY'RE NAE USE TAE THE THEATRE.
LATER—
THERE'S BIG TAM THE TOUGH.
HAND OWER YER PURSE, WIFIE!
TAK' THAT, YE BIG APE!
OUCH!
I'LL BELT YE FOR THAT, YE WEE NYAFF!
DINNA BOTHER. A FRIEND O' MINE'S STANDIN' JIST ROOND THERE.
HUMPH! I'LL GET YE SOME OTHER TIME.
I CAN SEE THOSE HATS ARE GOIN' TAE COME IN HANDY.
THAT WIS AWFY CLEVER O' YE, SONNY. TAK' TEN PENCE FOR YER TROUBLE.
OH, POOR SACHA!
JINGS!
I'VE GOT JIST THE THING FOR YE HERE, MISSUS.
THIS HAT SHOULD KEEP YER WEE DOG WARM TILL YE GET HAME.
THANK YOU. HERE, TAKE FIFTY PENCE!
HOW'S BUSINESS, MR PHILLIPS?
SUCH IS THE RESURGENCE OF APPRECIATION OF TRUE ART THAT MY CAP IS UNABLE TO COPE WITH THE CASH FLOW SITUATION.
FOWK LIKE YER BONNY PICTURES BUT YER CAP CANNA COPE WI' THE CASH, EH?
TRY THIS FOR SIZE. IT SHOULD TAK' CARE O' YER MONEY.
I AM MOST GRATEFUL, WULLIE. HERE'S TWENTY PENCE.
LUCA
CAFE
BEST ICE CREAM
OOPS!
SORRY, TONI!
SORRY, YES, BUTTA LOOK ATTA MY SIGN.
CAFE
I'LL HELP YE OOT, TONI!
USE THIS UPSIDE DOON.
D
ITSA VERRA FINE! EVEN GOTTA MY INITIAL ON IT UPSIDE DOWN.
TONI DELUCA
CAFE
I GIVE YOU ALLA DA ICE CREAM YOU WANT, EH? YOU MY SPECIAL GUEST, OKAY?
HA-HA! I'M PRETTY GOOD AT HAT-TRICKS, EH?

*Wull's oot tae see the fitba', free—*

*Up high on stilts, or in a tree!*

UNITED ARE PLAYIN' THISTLE THE DAY.
PLENTY O' SPECTATORS, THAT'S BRAW.
UNITED A.F.C.
WI' A THOSE FOWK IN THERE, NAEBODY WILL NOTICE ME HAEIN' A FREE LOOK AT THE GEMME . . .
MOVE ALONG, WULLIE. YE CANNA STAND THERE LIKE THAT.
. . . EXCEPT MAYBE P.C. MURDOCH.
ACH, IT'S A'RICHT FOR HIM—HE GETS IN FOR NOTHIN'!
I KEN WHIT I'LL DAE.
Wullie's Shed.
I CAN SEE RICHT OWER THE FENCE WI' MY STILTS.
OOYAH!
GET OOT O' HERE, YE WEE PEST!
WULLIE'S BOUND TAE TURN UP AGAIN. HE'LL NEVER GIE UP TRYIN' TAE SEE THE GEMME FOR NOTHIN'!
OUCH!
SO THERE YE ARE, YE WEE MONKEY. COME DOON THIS MINUTE!
TIME TAE GO, I THINK!
WELL, THAT'S THE GEMME STARTED, AND WULLIE'S NO' GOT IN YET.
MICHTY ME! AN EARTHQUAKE!
SO! TUNNELLIN' YER WAY IN, EH?
YE DINNA GIE UP EASILY, DO YE? I'LL GIE YE FULL MARKS FOR TRYIN', BUT NONE O' YER WEE SCHEMES HAS WORKED . . .
. . . SO HERE'S THE MONEY TAE GET IN. AWA' YE GO AN' ENJOY THE MATCH.
NO THANKS. PAYIN' TAE GET IN IS NAE FUN AT A'!
I WENT UP TAE MY AUNTIE JEAN'S—HER HOOSE OVERLOOKS THE GROUND. UNITED WON 3-0!

Will Wullie's wellies leak or no'?—
That's what oor laddie wants tae know!
AH'M AWA' TAE TEST MY NEW WELLIES!
THE STOORIE BURN'LL DAE FINE TAE SEE IF THEY LET IN OR NO'.
NO, SONNY, YE'LL GET YER FEET WET.
GRAB!!
YOU JUST CROSS THERE. IT'S MUCH SAFER.
THANKS FUR NOTHIN'.
AH'LL GO PADDLIN' IN THE SEA.
TO THE BEACH
JINGS! THE TIDE'S OOT! AH'LL NO' HAE THE STRENGTH TAE PADDLE ONCE AH WALK OOT THERE.
PUDDOCK POND'LL DAE FINE!
HERE GOES!
HEY! YE CANNA JUMP IN THERE. THERE'S A RED-NECKED WHOOPING SPARROW-DUCK NESTING HERE—THE FIRST IN SCOTLAND!
THEY'RE SURE TAE HAE WATER IN THERE.
GARDEN CENTRE
JIST THE JOB!
IN WE GO!
HELP MA BOAB! WHIT'S GOIN' ON?
THAT'S JIST A MIRROR THAT LOOKS LIKE WATER.
I GIE UP! I'M CHANGING BACK TO MY TACKETTY BOOTS!
JUST AS WELL I'M OOT O' MY WELLIES. THERE'S NAE SIGN O' RAIN!
OH, NO!
IT'S NO' FUNNY!

*Though through the toon Oor Wullie flies—*

*It seems he needs MORE exercise!*

HE'S STILL IN BED!
COME ON, WULLIE! GET UP! IT'S TEN TAE NINE! YE'LL BE LATE FOR SCHOOL!
MICHTY! I'LL NEED TAE HURRY TAE BE IN FOR NINE!
BETTER GET DRESSED.
'SCUSE ME, PA!
Wullie's Hoose
I KEN A GUID SHORT CUT TAE SCHOOL.
THIS'LL SAVE ME BAGS O' TIME!
WONDER WHIT THE TIME IS?
YE CANNA COME THIS WAY, SONNY, IT'S FOR VEHICLES ONLY. PEDESTRIANS GO THE LANG WAY ROOND.
CAUTION ROAD WORKS
THAT'S A'RICHT! I'M A CARTWHEEL, NOO!
JINGS! HOW DAE I GET PAST THIS, THOUGH?
WET CONCRETE
I DINNA WANT MY WET CONCRETE MESSED UP! ONE FOOTPRINT IN THERE, AN' I'LL BELT YER LUG!
A FEW HANDPRINTS WINNA MATTER, THEN, EH?
HA-HA! SEE YE, MISTER!
SCHOOL
I CANNA HAE MUCH TIME LEFT, NOO!
WHEW! JUST MADE IT! PECH! MICHTY ME—I'M WORN OOT!
SLEEPING IN CLASS, WILLIAM? YOU SHOULD TAKE SOME EXERCISE IN THE MORNING TO WAKEN YOU UP!
MAIR EXERCISE? HUH!

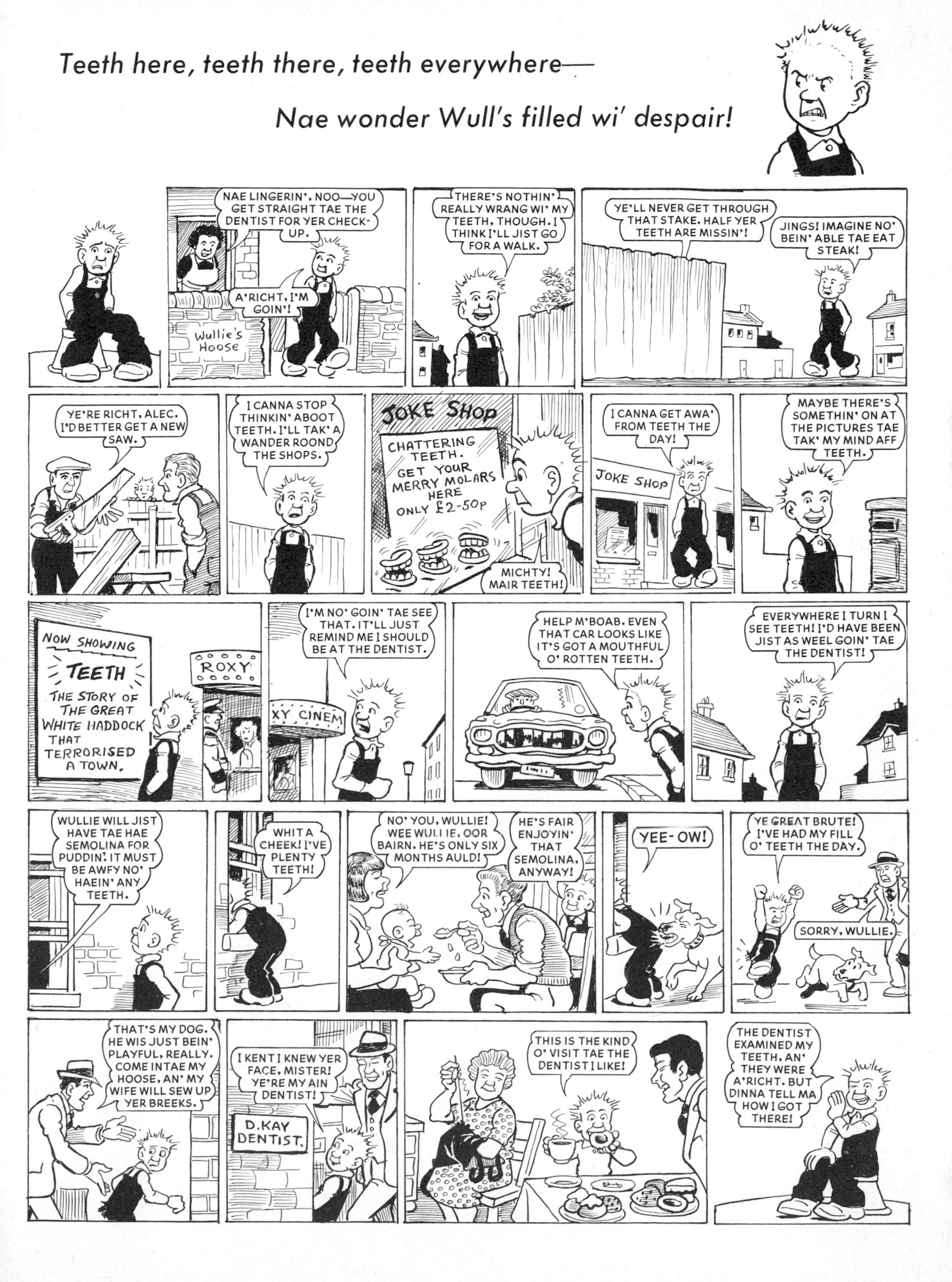
Teeth here, teeth there, teeth everywhere—
Nae wonder Wull's filled wi' despair!
NAE LINGERIN', NOO—YOU GET STRAIGHT TAE THE DENTIST FOR YER CHECK-UP.
A'RICHT, I'M GOIN'!
Wullie's Hoose
THERE'S NOTHIN' REALLY WRANG WI' MY TEETH, THOUGH. I THINK I'LL JIST GO FOR A WALK.
YE'LL NEVER GET THROUGH THAT STAKE. HALF YER TEETH ARE MISSIN'!
JINGS! IMAGINE NO' BEIN' ABLE TAE EAT STEAK!
YE'RE RICHT, ALEC. I'D BETTER GET A NEW SAW.
I CANNA STOP THINKIN' ABOOT TEETH. I'LL TAK' A WANDER ROOND THE SHOPS.
JOKE SHOP
CHATTERING TEETH. GET YOUR MERRY MOLARS HERE ONLY £2-50p
MICHTY! MAIR TEETH!
I CANNA GET AWA' FROM TEETH THE DAY!
JOKE SHOP
MAYBE THERE'S SOMETHIN' ON AT THE PICTURES TAE TAK' MY MIND AFF TEETH.
NOW SHOWING TEETH THE STORY OF THE GREAT WHITE HADDOCK THAT TERRORISED A TOWN.
ROXY
I'M NO' GOIN' TAE SEE THAT. IT'LL JUST REMIND ME I SHOULD BE AT THE DENTIST.
XY CINEM
HELP M'BOAB. EVEN THAT CAR LOOKS LIKE IT'S GOT A MOUTHFUL O' ROTTEN TEETH.
EVERYWHERE I TURN I SEE TEETH! I'D HAVE BEEN JIST AS WEEL GOIN' TAE THE DENTIST!
WULLIE WILL JIST HAVE TAE HAE SEMOLINA FOR PUDDIN'. IT MUST BE AWFY NO' HAEIN' ANY TEETH.
WHIT A CHEEK! I'VE PLENTY TEETH!
NO' YOU, WULLIE! WEE WULLIE, OOR BAIRN. HE'S ONLY SIX MONTHS AULD!
HE'S FAIR ENJOYIN' THAT SEMOLINA, ANYWAY!
YEE-OW!
YE GREAT BRUTE! I'VE HAD MY FILL O' TEETH THE DAY.
SORRY, WULLIE.
THAT'S MY DOG. HE WIS JUST BEIN' PLAYFUL, REALLY. COME INTAE MY HOOSE, AN' MY WIFE WILL SEW UP YER BREEKS.
I KENT I KNEW YER FACE, MISTER! YE'RE MY AIN DENTIST!
D. KAY DENTIST.
THIS IS THE KIND O' VISIT TAE THE DENTIST I LIKE!
THE DENTIST EXAMINED MY TEETH, AN' THEY WERE A'RICHT. BUT DINNA TELL MA HOW I GOT THERE!

*After keeping things so quiet—*

*Oor lad would sleep right through a riot!*

HEY, WULLIE! I'M ON THE NICHT SHIFT THE NICHT, AN' I'LL GIE YE FIFTY PENCE IF YE KEEP A' THING QUIET WHILE I'M ASLEEP.
YE'RE ON!
CRIVVENS! THAT BAIRN'S GOIN' TAE START HOWLIN'!
THIS STICK O' ROCK SHOULD KEEP YOU QUIET.
THERE'S WEE ECK WI' A DRUM!
BONK!
ECK, STOP! OUCH!
LOOK AT A' THIS BRAW CROCKERY I GOT AT THE JUMBLE SALE, WULLIE.
LOOK OUT, MA!
PHEW! A BREAKIN' CUP WID MAK' AN AWFY DIN!
AA- AA—
HE'S GOIN' TAE SNEEZE!
BETTER BE QUICK.
MUFFLED SNEEZE
SORRY, MISTER. GOT TAE KEEP THINGS QUIET.
AND NOW LET'S HEAR THE LATEST FROM THE SCREAMING YETTIES!
JINGS! THAT SONG'S DEAFENIN'!
SORRY, SOAPY. YE'LL HAVE TAE CHANGE CHANNELS.
CLICK!
THAT'S MUCH BETTER.
ROCK-A-BYE BABY ON THE TREE TOP...
AT LAST—
GUID LAD, WULLIE. I'VE HAD A BRAW SLEEP, HERE'S YER MONEY.
TA! I'M WORN OOT. THINK I'LL HAE A SEAT ON MY BUCKET.
TA-TA-RAA!
TA-TA-RAA!
BOOM!
BOOM!
YAK! YAK!
TOOT! TOOT!
ROAR!
WHINE!
DRRR!
WHO NEEDS PEACE AND QUIET?
SNORE!
WOOF! WOOF!
MEOW!

*Oor Wull gets in a proper tizz—*

*Just trying to find what time it is!*

JINGS! I'VE JIST REMEMBERED! I'VE TAE MEET UNCLE TAM AT THE STATION AT QUARTER PAST ONE!
WONDER WHIT TIME IT IS NOW? THERE'S ECK, I'LL ASK HIM.
SEE MY NEW WATCH, WULLIE? IT GIES YE THE TEMPERATURE, ALTITUDE, DISTANCE TAE THE MOON AN' THE PRICE O' FISHCAKES IN HONG KONG.
AYE, BUT WHIT TIME IS IT?
I'VE NO' WORKED OOT HOW TAE TELL THE TIME WI' IT, YET, ACTUALLY.
ACH, YOU'RE NAE HELP!
I'LL SEE THE STEEPLE CLOCK IN JIST A MINUTE.
AW, NO! THEY'RE REPAIRIN' THE CLOCK!
GREAT. SOAPY'S GOT A TRANNY! I'LL GET THE TIME AFF THAT.
IN TWO MINUTES, IT WILL BE EXACTLY . . .
I'LL GET THE RICHT TIME NOW!
WOOOOOO!
HELP M'BOAB! I CANNA HEAR FOR THON HOOOTER!
THEY'RE KNOCKIN' AFF AT THE FACTORY, THOUGH. SOME O' THAE MEN'LL KEN THE TIME.
EXCUSE ME. CAN YOU TELL ME THE RIGHT . . .
WHOOOSH!
WOW!
HUH! THEY WERE IN SUCH A RUSH THEY DIDNA HEAR ME!
CRIVVENS! IT'S HALF PAST ONE BY THE STATION CLOCK. UNCLE TAM'S THERE WAITIN'.
I'M AWFY SORRY I'M LATE, UNCLE TAM. I DIDNA KEN WHIT TIME IT WAS.
I KEN WHIT TIME IT IS—TIME YE HAD A WATCH, WULLIE! HERE.
MY, WHIT A BRAW PRESENT! I'LL PUT IT ON.
AW, NO! I FORGOT— PAW GAVE ME HIS WATCH THIS MORNIN' SO'S I'D BE ON TIME!
NOW I'VE GOT THE TIME IN STEREO!

*Archie Ologist? Who's he?—*

*Just tak' a look below and see!*

HE'S AWA' FOR A WANDER.
DRUMTOGLE ROMAN FORT
JINGS! LOOK AT A' THE BRAW STUFF THEY'RE FINDIN'.
HERE, THIS JAR'S GOT A SET O' FALSERS IN IT!
YESH! MINE! I JUST DROPPED THEM!
I WOULDNA MIND BEIN' AN ARCHIE OLOGIST MASEL'!
KEEP OOT. ARCHIE OLOGIST AT WORK!
I'LL TRY DIGGIN' HERE.
WHIT'S THIS? A ROMAN SOLDIER'S RIFLE MAYBE?
CRIVVENS! LOOKS MAIR LIKE THE REMAINS O' AN ACTUAL ROMAN GENERAL!
HEY! SO IT'S YOURS, IS IT?
ACH, WEEL. THAT DOG'S CALLED CAESER, ANYWAY.
HERE'S SOMETHIN' ELSE! A ROMAN STATUE, MAYBE?
HUH! DE LUCA'S DAIRY. AT LEAST IT SOUNDS ITALIAN.
I'LL KEEP GOIN'. THERE'S BOUND TAE BE SOMETHIN' HERE. THIS PART O' SCOTLAND WIS CRAWLIN' WI' ROMANS.
I KNEW IT! LOOKS LIKE PART O' A CHARIOT WHEEL.
IT'S GOT WRITIN' ON IT! R...O...IT MUST BE ROMAN!
ROAMIN' IN THE GLOAMIN' BY HARRY LAUDER. WHIT A LET-DOON.
NOTHIN' BUT AULD JUNK. I'M FED UP WI' ROMANS AN' STUFF FROM ITALY.
YEUCH! THAT'S A' I NEED! ECK WILSON IN HIS WEE ITALIAN CAR!
COME AWA' IN, WULLIE. WAIT TILL YE SEE WHIT'S FOR TEA.
AW, NO!
WHIT'S WRANG WI' HIM? HE USUALLY LOVES SPAGHETTI!
I GOT MA TAE MAK' MACARONI INSTEAD.
SSH! DINNA TELL HIM THAT'S ITALIAN AN' A'!

*Beware Oor Wullie's Leisure Centre—*

*There are shocks galore for all who enter!*

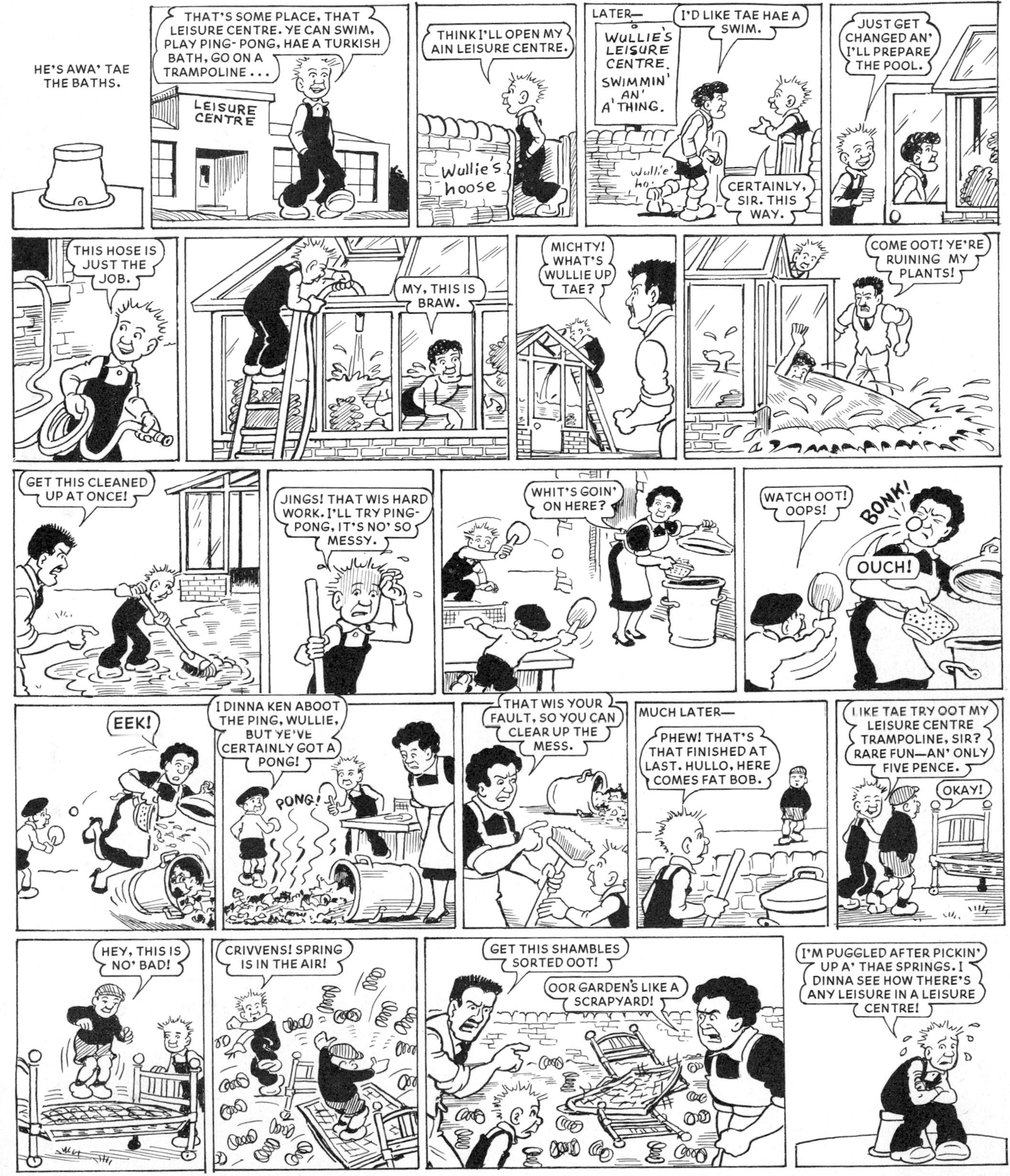

HE'S AWA' TAE THE BATHS.
THAT'S SOME PLACE, THAT LEISURE CENTRE. YE CAN SWIM, PLAY PING-PONG, HAE A TURKISH BATH, GO ON A TRAMPOLINE . . .
LEISURE CENTRE
THINK I'LL OPEN MY AIN LEISURE CENTRE.
Wullie's hoose
LATER—
WULLIE'S LEISURE CENTRE. SWIMMIN' AN' A' THING.
I'D LIKE TAE HAE A SWIM.
CERTAINLY, SIR. THIS WAY.
JUST GET CHANGED AN' I'LL PREPARE THE POOL.
THIS HOSE IS JUST THE JOB.
MY, THIS IS BRAW.
MICHTY! WHAT'S WULLIE UP TAE?
COME OOT! YE'RE RUINING MY PLANTS!
GET THIS CLEANED UP AT ONCE!
JINGS! THAT WIS HARD WORK. I'LL TRY PING-PONG, IT'S NO' SO MESSY.
WHIT'S GOIN' ON HERE?
WATCH OOT! OOPS!
BONK!
OUCH!
EEK!
I DINNA KEN ABOOT THE PING, WULLIE, BUT YE'VE CERTAINLY GOT A PONG!
PONG!
THAT WIS YOUR FAULT, SO YOU CAN CLEAR UP THE MESS.
MUCH LATER—
PHEW! THAT'S THAT FINISHED AT LAST. HULLO, HERE COMES FAT BOB.
LIKE TAE TRY OOT MY LEISURE CENTRE TRAMPOLINE, SIR? RARE FUN—AN' ONLY FIVE PENCE.
OKAY!
HEY, THIS IS NO' BAD!
CRIVVENS! SPRING IS IN THE AIR!
GET THIS SHAMBLES SORTED OOT!
OOR GARDEN'S LIKE A SCRAPYARD!
I'M PUGGLED AFTER PICKIN' UP A' THAE SPRINGS. I DINNA SEE HOW THERE'S ANY LEISURE IN A LEISURE CENTRE!

*Why that medal? Ah, that's the question—*

*Of all the answers, Wull's is the best yin!*

THERE THEY ARE! ANY MINUTE NOW!
HERE, WULLIE! WHIT DID YE GET THAT MEDAL FOR?
ACH, I'M OWER MODEST TAE TELL YE! SEE IF YE CAN GUESS!
I KEN, BOAB! IT WIS FOR HELPIN' THE POLIS . . .
I MIND THE TIME YE SAVED AULD MURDOCH WHEN THE INSPECTOR NEAR CAUGHT HIM HAEIN' A FLY SMOKE!
NA! NA! IT'S NO' FOR THAT!
THEN IT MUST BE A BRAVERY MEDAL!
YE GOT IT FOR THAT TIME YE LICKED BAITH THE MURPHY LADS SINGLE HANDED!
AYE, BUT YE'VE FORGOTTEN ONE THING, BOAB . . .
THEIR WEE SISTER GOT HIM BACK!
SHE DESERVES A MEDAL FOR HER STRENGTH! WHIT A SKELP SHE GAVE ME!
THEN IT MUST BE FOR STORY TELLIN'! I MIND WHEN YE TOLD US THAT ONE DAY YE SAVED THE WHOLE TOWN FROM A FLOOD, RUSHED UP TAE DRUMTOGLE TAE BEAT OOT A FOREST FIRE, THEN CAPTURED THREE SPIES SAILIN' UP STOORIE BURN IN A SUBMARINE!
HA-HA! EVEN I COULDN'T TELL SUCH A TALL TALE AS THAT!
WELL, MAYBE I SHOULD GET A MEDAL FOR TELLIN' TALL STORIES, BUT THAT'S NO' WHIT IT'S FOR EITHER.
IT MUST BE FOR SCORIN' THE WINNIN' GOAL IN THE SCHOOLS' CUP FINAL, THEN! NAE SCORE WI' ONLY TWA MINUTES TAE GO. WE TOOK A GOAL KICK . . .
—AND THE BA' BOUNCED AFF YOU— INTAE OOR GOAL!
THAT'S NO' FUNNY! GUESS AGAIN!
WE GIE UP! TELL US WHIT YE GOT IT FOR.
I GOT IT TAE HOLD UP MY DUNGAREES TILL MA CAN SEW ON A BUTTON THAT FELL AFF!

You'll soon see why Oor Wullie's glum—
Wee Jeemy is a DEAR wee chum!
WONDER WHIT I CAN SPEND MY POCKET MONEY ON?
PA FORGOT HIS SANDWICHES, WULLIE. BE A GUID LAD AN' TAK' THEM TAE HIM.
THIS'LL NO' TAK' LANG.
OH, NO!
I FORGOT JEEMY WIS IN MY POCKET!
CHEWED
SNACK BAR
I'LL HAE TAE BUY PA MAIR SANDWICHES.
CRIVVENS! IT'S AULD MURDOCH!
HE'LL NO' FIND ME IN HERE!
AYE, AYE, I KEN THAT NOISE!
SQUEAK! SQUEAK
OOT YE COME, WULLIE! I HEARD JEEMY MILES AWA'!
TRAITOR!
COME ON, WULLIE. DINNA THINK YE'RE GETTIN' AWA' WI' NO' BUYIN' TICKETS FOR THE PRIZE DRAW.
LATER—
AWA' DOON TAE THE SHOPS AN' GET ME SOME JAM, WULLIE.
HERE YE ARE, MR JONES.
THANK YOU, WILLIAM.
HA-HA-HA! STOP IT, WILL YE?
I'VE DROPPED THE JAR! HA-HA-HA!
YE WEE NUISANCE! LOOK WHIT YE'VE MADE ME DAE WI' YER TICKLIN'! NOW I'LL HAE TAE BUY ANITHER POT WI' MY AIN MONEY!
ONLY TEN PENCE O' MY POCKET MONEY LEFT!
OOPS!
HELP M'BOAB! IT'S AWA' INTAE THON HOLE JEEMY MADE IN THE SKIRTIN'-BOARD!
MY, WULLIE—IT MUST BE GREAT HAVING A WEE MOOSE AS A PET! DOGS COST YOU A FORTUNE!
PET FOODS
HUH!

*Oor Wullie spreads the news round fast—*

*The men from Mars are here at last!*

LIBRARY
HI, BOAB!
HIYA, WULLIE!
LOOK AT THIS, WULLIE. IT'S A BOOK WRITTEN BY A MAN WHO SAYS SPACEMEN HAVE LANDED!
AWA'! YE DINNA BELIEVE THAT, DO YE?
HAVE YE EVER HEARD ANYTHING SO DAFT? REAL SPACEMEN—HA-HA!
THERE'S NOTHING LIKE A GOOD, CLEAN LANDING.
YES, ONCE THE LANDING IS OVER, THE REST IS EASY!
HELP M'BOAB! THEY'VE LANDED AFTER A'!
I'D BETTER RUN AN' WARN A'BODY!
WELL, NOW WE'VE DONE THE LANDING, WE'D BETTER GO BACK AN' SCRUB THE STAIRS.
AYE, LET'S GET ON WI' IT!
WULLIE, LOOK . . . !
OH, NO!
IT'S A TRAP! THERE'S A MARTIAN BACK THERE KEEPIN' SOAPY COVERED!
I DON'T THINK WULLIE WANTS TO HELP CLEAN YOUR CAR, MR GRAY!
WULLIE, WULLIE . . . HELP!
THEY'VE CAPTURED WEE ECK AN' A'! THEY'RE GETTIN' HIM READY TAE GO INTAE SPACE!
I MUST GET HELP!
I WISH WULLIE HAD STAYED TAE HELP! MY MA'LL KILL ME WHEN SHE FINDS OOT I'VE GOT THE GOLDFISH BOWL STUCK ON MY HEID!
P.C. MURDOCH! THE MARTIANS HAVE LANDED!
WHIT?
YE'VE GOT TAE HELP! THE MARTIANS HAVE CAPTURED SOAPY AN' ECK!
DINNA BE DAFT! AWA' AN' STOP WASTIN' MY TIME!
HEY, WULLIE! COME BACK! THERE'S A MARTIAN BAND COMING UP THE STREET!
A BAND O' MARTIANS, EH? I TOLD YE THEY'D LANDED!
NO' A MARTIAN BAND—A MARCHIN' BAND. THEY'RE GOIN' DOON TAE PLAY IN THE PARK!
AN' THERE'S SOAPY AN' ECK! THEY'VE NO' BEEN CAPTURED AFTER A'!
THIS IS DEFINITELY THE ONLY KIND O' "MARTIAN" I LIKE!

*A bath for Wullie? Not a chance—*

*He leads his Ma a merry dance!*

BATH TIME, WULLIE!
NAE CHANCE! TIME TAE GO!
PUIR LADDIE!
I'LL HIDE IN HERE! I DINNA NEED A BATH, I'M NO' EVEN DIRTY!
COAL SHED
COAL SHED
WELL, NO' DIRTY ENOUGH FOR A BATH, ANYWAY!
COAL SHED
MA'LL NEVER FIND ME IN HERE.
YEUCH, WHIT A PONG!
I'LL HAE TAE FIND SOMEPLACE CLEANER!
SO—
THIS SHOULD BE SAFE ENOUGH.
NAEBODY'LL NOTICE IF I JUST DUMP MY SOOT AN' STUFF IN HERE.
NOW I KEN WHIT KIND O' TREE THIS IS—AN ASH!
COME BACK HERE, YE WEE MONKEY!
IT'S MA! I'LL LOSE HER IN THE PARK!
I'LL NIP IN HERE AN' MAK' A CLEAN GETAWAY!
WHAUR IS HE? I CANNA SPEND A' NICHT CHASIN' HIM!
POOH! THAT DOES IT! I'D RATHER BE COVERED WI' HOT WATER THAN ANY MAIR O' THIS STUFF!
MA—CAN I HAE A BATH, PLEASE?
WULLIE! WHIT'S COME OWER YE?
JUST ABOOT A'THING'S COME OWER ME! COAL, RUBBISH, SOOT . . .
NEVER THOUGHT I'D BE PLEASED TAE TAK' A BATH!
BUT—
IT'S OKAY, WULLIE! I'VE SAVED YE FROM THE BATH! I USED A' THE HOT WATER!
HMPH!

*Wull does his best to save these pies—*

*But he still gets a big surprise!*

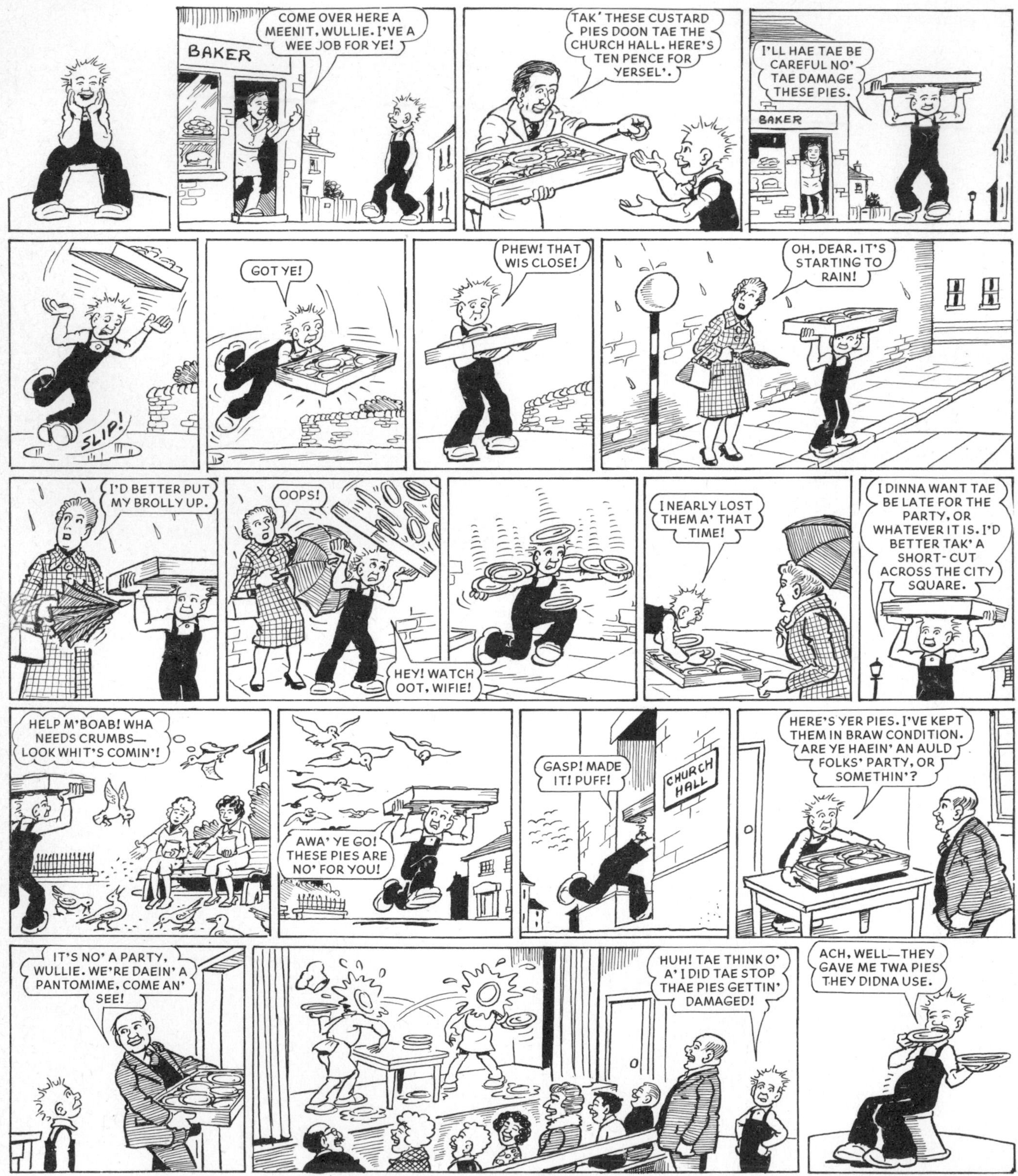

COME OVER HERE A MEENIT, WULLIE. I'VE A WEE JOB FOR YE!
BAKER
TAK' THESE CUSTARD PIES DOON TAE THE CHURCH HALL. HERE'S TEN PENCE FOR YERSEL'.
I'LL HAE TAE BE CAREFUL NO' TAE DAMAGE THESE PIES.
BAKER
SLIP!
GOT YE!
PHEW! THAT WIS CLOSE!
OH, DEAR. IT'S STARTING TO RAIN!
I'D BETTER PUT MY BROLLY UP.
OOPS!
HEY! WATCH OOT, WIFIE!
I NEARLY LOST THEM A' THAT TIME!
I DINNA WANT TAE BE LATE FOR THE PARTY, OR WHATEVER IT IS. I'D BETTER TAK' A SHORT-CUT ACROSS THE CITY SQUARE.
HELP M'BOAB! WHA NEEDS CRUMBS— LOOK WHIT'S COMIN'!
AWA' YE GO! THESE PIES ARE NO' FOR YOU!
GASP! MADE IT! PUFF!
CHURCH HALL
HERE'S YER PIES. I'VE KEPT THEM IN BRAW CONDITION. ARE YE HAEIN' AN AULD FOLKS' PARTY, OR SOMETHIN'?
IT'S NO' A PARTY, WULLIE. WE'RE DAEIN' A PANTOMIME, COME AN' SEE!
HUH! TAE THINK O' A' I DID TAE STOP THAE PIES GETTIN' DAMAGED!
ACH, WELL—THEY GAVE ME TWA PIES THEY DIDNA USE.

*It's a proper laughalot—*

*When Wullie wants tae sail his yacht!*

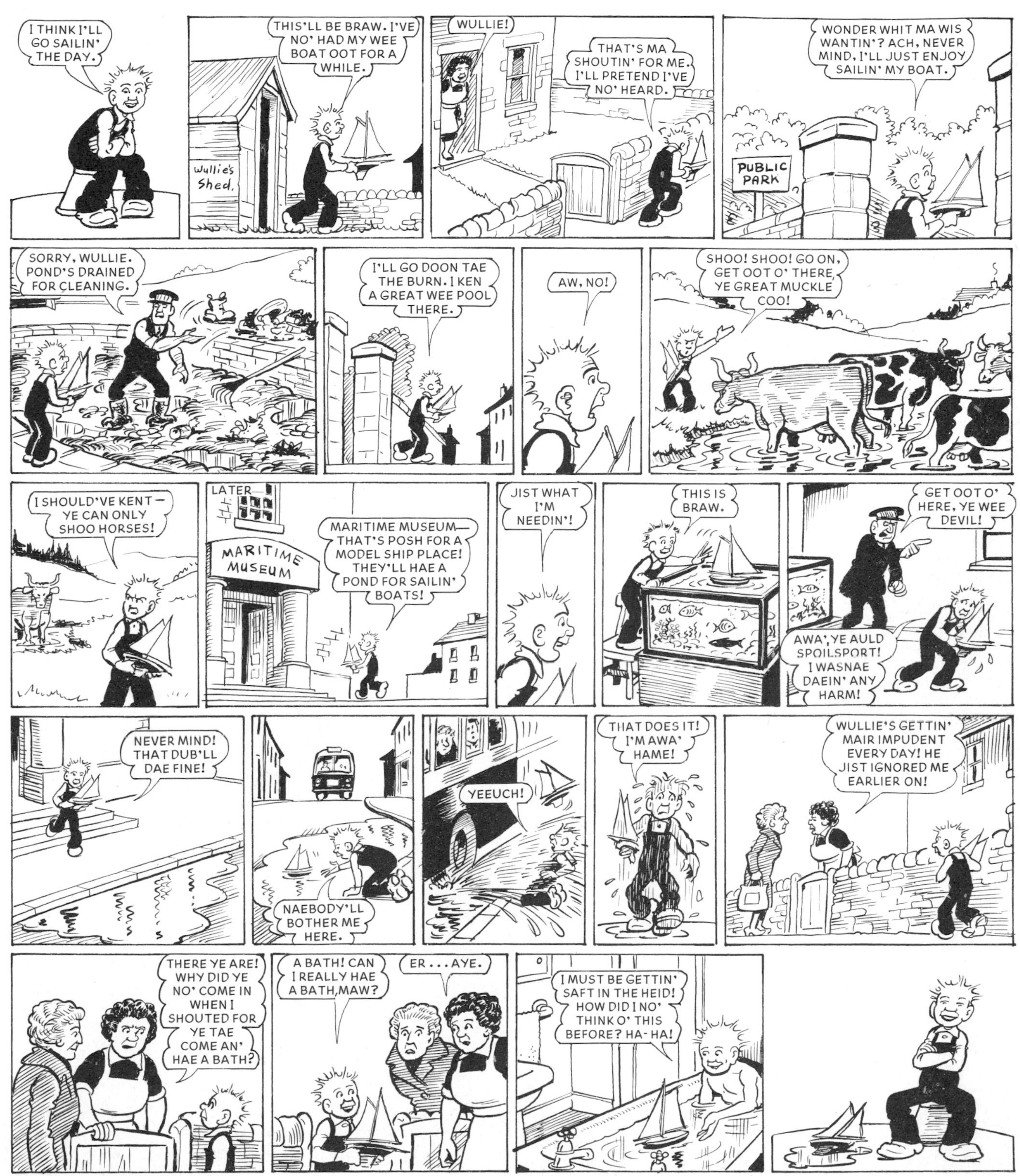

I THINK I'LL GO SAILIN' THE DAY.
THIS'LL BE BRAW. I'VE NO' HAD MY WEE BOAT OOT FOR A WHILE.
Wullie's Shed.
WULLIE!
THAT'S MA SHOUTIN' FOR ME. I'LL PRETEND I'VE NO' HEARD.
WONDER WHIT MA WIS WANTIN'? ACH, NEVER MIND, I'LL JUST ENJOY SAILIN' MY BOAT.
PUBLIC PARK
SORRY, WULLIE. POND'S DRAINED FOR CLEANING.
I'LL GO DOON TAE THE BURN. I KEN A GREAT WEE POOL THERE.
AW, NO!
SHOO! SHOO! GO ON, GET OOT O' THERE, YE GREAT MUCKLE COO!
I SHOULD'VE KENT — YE CAN ONLY SHOO HORSES!
LATER
MARITIME MUSEUM
MARITIME MUSEUM— THAT'S POSH FOR A MODEL SHIP PLACE! THEY'LL HAE A POND FOR SAILIN' BOATS!
JIST WHAT I'M NEEDIN'!
THIS IS BRAW.
GET OOT O' HERE, YE WEE DEVIL!
AWA', YE AULD SPOILSPORT! I WASNAE DAEIN' ANY HARM!
NEVER MIND! THAT DUB'LL DAE FINE!
NAEBODY'LL BOTHER ME HERE.
YEEUCH!
THAT DOES IT! I'M AWA' HAME!
WULLIE'S GETTIN' MAIR IMPUDENT EVERY DAY! HE JIST IGNORED ME EARLIER ON!
THERE YE ARE! WHY DID YE NO' COME IN WHEN I SHOUTED FOR YE TAE COME AN' HAE A BATH?
A BATH! CAN I REALLY HAE A BATH, MAW?
ER . . . AYE.
I MUST BE GETTIN' SAFT IN THE HEID! HOW DID I NO' THINK O' THIS BEFORE? HA-HA!

*Puir wee Wull. His luck is oot—*

*See his footwear get the boot!*

WULLIE! LOOK AT THE HOLES IN YER BOOTS. IT'S TIME YE GOT A NEW PAIR.
SEE MY NEW BOOTS! BRAW, EH?
...AN' LOOK AT THAE TACKETS!
I CAN TAP-DANCE AN' A'THING!
CLICK!
CLATTER!
WAKEN MY BAIRN, WOULD YE, YE WEE DEVIL!
OUCH! THIS NEVER HAPPENED TAE FRED ASTAIRE!
CRIVVENS! IT'S MASHER MACRAE!
HELP M'BOAB! THAE HEAVY TACKETS ARE SLOWIN' ME DOON!
GOT YE! I OWE YE A THUMPIN', WULLIE!
GULP!
BAH!
HEY, WULLIE! WANT A GEMME?
AYE, SURE!
BUT—
NO YE DON'T! YE'RE NO' GETTIN' THAE NEW BOOTS IN A MESS!
STILL, THEY MAK' BRAW SPARKS!
MICHTY ME! I'VE SET THAE LEAVES ALIGHT!
LUCKY I HAD MY HOSE HANDY!
AYE, BUT NO' FOR ME!
OH, NO! MA'LL BE WANTIN' ME FOR MY BATH!
HMM... WHIT'S THAT?
SQUEAK! SQUEAK!
COME ON, WULLIE. YER NEW BOOTS WERE SQUEAKIN'. THEY GAVE YE AWA'!
I'M GOIN' BACK TAE MY AULD BOOTS—AN' RUBBER SOLES!

*A sanctuary for birds? That's grand!—*

*But things don't go quite as Wull planned.*

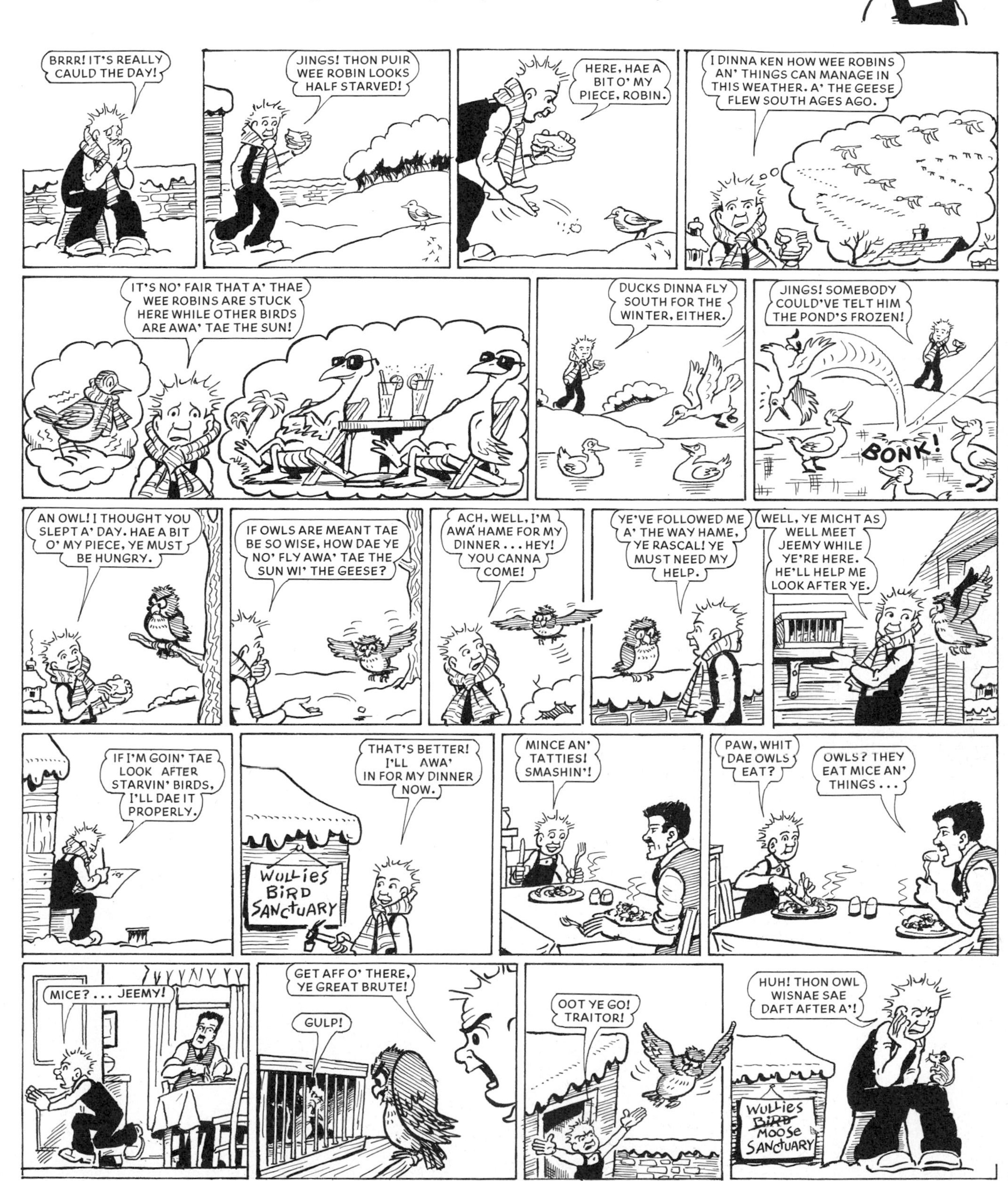

BRRR! IT'S REALLY CAULD THE DAY!
JINGS! THON PUIR WEE ROBIN LOOKS HALF STARVED!
HERE, HAE A BIT O' MY PIECE, ROBIN.
I DINNA KEN HOW WEE ROBINS AN' THINGS CAN MANAGE IN THIS WEATHER. A' THE GEESE FLEW SOUTH AGES AGO.
IT'S NO' FAIR THAT A' THAE WEE ROBINS ARE STUCK HERE WHILE OTHER BIRDS ARE AWA' TAE THE SUN!
DUCKS DINNA FLY SOUTH FOR THE WINTER, EITHER.
JINGS! SOMEBODY COULD'VE TELT HIM THE POND'S FROZEN!
BONK!
AN OWL! I THOUGHT YOU SLEPT A' DAY. HAE A BIT O' MY PIECE, YE MUST BE HUNGRY.
IF OWLS ARE MEANT TAE BE SO WISE, HOW DAE YE NO' FLY AWA' TAE THE SUN WI' THE GEESE?
ACH, WELL, I'M AWA' HAME FOR MY DINNER . . . HEY! YOU CANNA COME!
YE'VE FOLLOWED ME A' THE WAY HAME, YE RASCAL! YE MUST NEED MY HELP.
WELL, YE MICHT AS WELL MEET JEEMY WHILE YE'RE HERE. HE'LL HELP ME LOOK AFTER YE.
IF I'M GOIN' TAE LOOK AFTER STARVIN' BIRDS, I'LL DAE IT PROPERLY.
WULLIES BIRD SANCTUARY
THAT'S BETTER! I'LL AWA' IN FOR MY DINNER NOW.
MINCE AN' TATTIES! SMASHIN'!
PAW, WHIT DAE OWLS EAT?
OWLS? THEY EAT MICE AN' THINGS . . .
MICE? . . . JEEMY!
GET AFF O' THERE, YE GREAT BRUTE!
GULP!
OOT YE GO! TRAITOR!
HUH! THON OWL WISNAE SAE DAFT AFTER A'!
WULLIES ~~BIRD~~ MOOSE SANCTUARY

*Just when it seems disaster looms—*

*Up come Wullie's quick-grow blooms!*

HE'S AT SCHOOL
NOW TOMORROW I WANT YOU TO BRING IN YOUR SPRING FLOWERS— REMEMBER I ASKED YOU ALL TO PLANT BULBS IN THE AUTUMN.
JINGS! I FORGOT TAE PLANT ANYTHIN'! WHIT CAN I DAE?
HA-HA! YE'RE IN TROUBLE, WULLIE! OOR BLOOMS ARE FAIR SPROUTIN'!
SCHOOL
I'LL SEE IF THERE'S ANY BULBS IN THE SHED.
HUH—PLENTY O' AULD LIGHT BULBS! HAUD ON, THOUGH, HERE'S SOME FLOOER BULBS.
WHIT THEY NEED IS HEAT TAE BRING THEM ON FOR THE MORN.
JINGS! IT'S BOILIN' SITTIN' THIS CLOSE TAE THE FIRE.
PHEW! WHIT A HEAT! AN' THE ONLY SIGN O' ANY FLOOERS IS ME GOIN' ROSY RED!
LATER—
WHAUR'S THE HAIR DRIER GONE?
FUNNY, THAT SOUNDS LIKE THE HAIR DRIER IN WULLIE'S ROOM!
GIE ME THAT THING AT ONCE!
AW, MAW!
I'LL GO DOON AN' SEE BIG JIM ON HIS ALLOTMENT. HE'LL KEN WHIT TAE DAE!
Wullie's Hoose
THE BEST THING YE CAN DAE FOR THESE BULBS IS BUY A POUND O' MINCE—THEY'RE ONIONS, NO' DAFFODILS!
HELP M'BOAB!
WE'D BETTER MAK' SURE YE DINNA GET INTAE TROUBLE, WULLIE. HERE'S WHIT YE CAN DAE . . .
LATER . . .
YE CANNA BRING ON YER BULBS WI' A BONFIRE, WULLIE! YE'RE FAR TOO LATE!
AYE, YE'LL GET TOKYO THE MORN FOR NO HAVIN' FLOOERS!
JIST YOU WAIT! BURNIN' THIS STUFF WILL GET ME THE BEST FLOOERS IN THE CLASS!
NEXT DAY—
ALL RIGHT, BRING OUT YOUR BULBS AND I'LL GIVE YOU YOUR MARKS.
YUK-YUK! YE'RE FOR IT NOW, WULLIE!
IT'LL BE SIX O' THE BELT AN' A MILLION LINES AT LEAST!
EXCELLENT, WILLIAM! YOU GET TEN OUT OF TEN!
JINGS! THON BONFIRE MUST'VE WORKED AFTER A'!
HA-HA! BIG JIM GAVE ME SOME O' HIS ANE DAFFIES FOR HELPING HIM BURN HIS RUBBISH—BUT DINNA TELL BOB OR SOAPY.

*No matter where auld Murdoch is—*

*Oor Wullie gets him in a fizz!*

I'M GOIN' TAE GET A'BODY TAE SIGN MY PETITION!
HEY, BOAB! WILL YE SIGN MY PETITION?
AYE, SURE, WULLIE.
I'M AFF TAE STOORIE WOODS. ARE YE COMIN'?
OKAY!
LATER—
TUT! TUT! WULLIE'S AYE UP TAE SOMETHIN'!
SNAP!
MICHTY ME! IT'S BROKEN!
P.C. MURDOCH!
OOF!
YE WEE MONKEY! I'LL CATCH UP WI' YE!
NO' IF I CAN HELP IT!
SOAPY, WILL YE SIGN MY PETITION?
SURE, WULLIE!
HELP M'BOAB! I'VE LET IN A GOAL! THAT'S YOUR FAULT, WULLIE!
DINNA WORRY! I'LL JIST SCORE A GOAL TAE MAK' UP FOR IT!
THERE Y'ARE! ANE O' MY CLASSIC DIVIN' HEIDERS!
OOPS! THERE'S ANE O' THE POLICE FORCE'S CLASSIC BALDY HEIDERS!
WULLIE! YOU AGAIN!
YE WEE DEVIL! I'LL SOON FIND YE AGAIN!
HUH! MURDOCH, THE ACE DETECTIVE!
HIYA, ECK! LIKE TO SIGN MY PETITION?
OKAY, WULLIE.
COMIN' FISHIN' WI' ME, WULLIE?
AYE, THAT'LL BE BRAW!
I'LL HAE TAE MAK' A ROD, THOUGH!
NO FISHING
THERE'S A WHOPPER LURKIN' IN THERE, ECK.
LATER—
YAHOO! I'VE CAUGHT HIM AT LAST!
SO HAVE I!
SPLAT!
CRIVVENS! IT'S AULD FISH-FACE AGAIN!
I'VE GOT YE NOW! YE'VE BEEN UP TAE MISCHIEF A' OWER THE PLACE TODAY!
ACH, I'VE ONLY BEEN COLLECTIN' SIGNATURES FOR MY PETITION . . .
. . . COMPLAININ' ABOOT THE LACK O' THINGS TAE DAE AROOND HERE!
HA-HA! THAT'S A LAUGH—YOU NO' BEIN' ABLE TAE FIND ANYTHIN' TAE DAE! HA-HA!
I GAVE P.C. MURDOCH SUCH A GUID LAUGH, HE LET ME AFF!

*Help m' boab! What's happenin' here?—*

*When Wull's around, folk disappear!*

OH, NO! THERE'S P.C. MURDOCH! HE'S AFTER ME FOR BREAKIN' A WINDIE! I'D BETTER HIDE!
TAILOR
NAE SIGN O' WULLIE ABOOT HERE.
TAILOR
CAN I HELP YOU, MADAM?
AYE, I'LL TAK' THESE DUNGAREES, PLEASE.
NA, YE'LL NO'! THESE BREEKS ARE MINE!
GASP!
WULLIE! TIME FOR YER BATH!
TIME TAE GO, YE MEAN!
Wullies Hoose
I'LL HIDE HERE. MA'LL SOON GIE UP AN' GO BACK IN.
HELP M'BOAB! WHIT'S THAT?
TIME I GAVE MY CAR A WASH.
HUH! I'M DROOKIT! I GOT A SHOWER INSTEAD O' A BATH!
MICHTY! IT'S MASHER Mc TURK! HE'S DUE ME A CLOBBERIN'!
THIS HAS AYE BEEN A GUID HIDIN' PLACE!
OW! IT WIS A GUID HIDIN' PLACE AFORE THESE WASPS MOVED IN, ANYWAY!
BETTER AVOID PA, OR HE'LL HAE ME DIGGIN' HIS GARDEN!
I'LL CRAWL ALONG THIS WAY . . .
OH! GULP . . . ER . . . HI, GOOD-LOOKIN'!
YEEUCH!
TRYIN' TAE AVOID FOWK LIKE THIS JUST DISNAE WORK OOT!
HEY, WULLIE! I'VE GOT SOMETHIN' FOR YE!
IT'S MR Mc PHEE FROM THE YOUTH CLUB—I DINNA HAE ANY REASON FOR AVOIDIN' HIM!
QUICK, MA! IT'S WULLIE! HE MUSTN'T SEE US!
HELP M'BOAB! IT'S WULLIE! I'M OFF!
OO-ER! THERE'S WULLIE! BETTER SCARPER!
MR Mc PHEE GAVE ME THESE. IF YE EVER WANT TAE AVOID FOWK, JUST TRY SELLIN' RAFFLE TICKETS! IT WORKS A TREAT!
ANYBODY WANT TAE BUY A RAFFLE TICKET?

*Wull's affy smart, but it's soon plain—*

*His " souper " schemes are all in vain!*

WULLIE!
BE A GUID LAD, AN' TAK' THIS HOT SOUP ROOND TAE GRANNY Mc PHEE— SHE'LL BE GLAD O' IT IN THIS CAULD WEATHER.
MY, THIS IS RARE AN' HOT!
IN FACT, IT'S BURNIN' MY HANDS!
I'LL NEED TAE PUT ON MY GLOVES.
THIS'LL BE JIST THE JOB . . . HEY!
COME BACK WI' THAT SOUP, YE DAFT SCUNNER!
PHEW! THAT WIS LUCKY! I'M BOILIN' NOW, BUT THE SOUP'S STONE CAULD!
MR WILSON—COULD YE GIE THIS PLATE O' SOUP A WEE HEAT-UP FOR ME?
PLUMBER
SURE, WULLIE!
THAT'S BRAW! THANKS, MR WILSON!
HEY, WULLIE! COME AN' HAE A WEE GEMME WI' US!
WELL, OKAY, THEN! I CANNA BIDE LANG, THOUGH!
THERE YE GO, BOAB!
I'LL HAE TAE GO NOW, LADS. I'M LATE A'READY.
HELP M'BOAB! THE SOUP'S GONE A' CAULD AGAIN!
I'LL GIE IT A HEAT ON THON FIRE.
DEMOLITION WORK IN PROGRESS
THIS'LL WARM IT UP IN NO TIME!
HEY, YOU! WHIT DAE YE THINK YE'RE DAEIN' WI' MY SPADE? GET OOT O' HERE!
HMM . . . THON STEAM MIGHT DAE INSTEAD!
THAT'S WARMIN' UP NICELY! I'LL JIST NIP ROOD TAE GRANNY Mc PHEE'S HOOSE, NOW.
OH, THANK YOU, WULLIE. I'LL JIST PUT IT ON THE WINDIE-SILL TAE COOL FOR HALF AN HOUR.
BUT . . . BUT I'VE BEEN TRYIN' TAE KEEP IT HOT!
THAT WAS AWFY GUID O' YE, WULLIE, BUT I'LL LET IT COOL AN' THEN PUT IT IN MY FREEZER. THEN I CAN USE IT NEXT WEEK SOME TIME.
GASP!
ACH, IT WIS WORTH IT AFTER A'—SHE GAVE ME THIS ICE LOLLY OOT O' HER FREEZER!

*. . . but no one wants to listen to—*

*The only lad whose story's true!*

OOH, SOAPY! WERE YOU REALLY IN A CRASH?
OCH, IT WASNAE AN AWFY BAD CRASH. I MANAGED TAE RESCUE SOME O' THE OTHER SURVIVORS AFORE I WENT FOR HELP.
WHIT'S HE BLETHERIN' ABOOT? HE WASNAE HURT IN A CRASH—HE FELL AFF HIS BIKE!
AND WAS THE BURGLAR YOU FOUGHT EVER FOUND, BOB?
NA! BUT WHEN I NABBED HIM BREAKIN' IN, I GAVE HIM A GUID BELTIN'. HE'LL NO BE BACK TAE OOR HOOSE!
WHIT A LOAD O' RUBBISH! HE GOT THON BLACK EYE WHEN JESSIE SMITH WALLOPED HIM FOR PINCHIN' HER SISTER'S SWEETS!
A'BODY JIST IGNORED ME! THEY'RE A' FALLIN' FOR BOAB AN' SOAPY'S STORIES!
OH, TIMMY, COME DOWN.
DINNA WORRY, LASSIE, I'LL FETCH YER CAT DOON!
OOPS! LOOKS LIKE WE'RE GOIN DOON THE QUICK WAY!
OOYAH!
TIMMY! YOU'RE SAFE AT LAST! THANK YOU, WILLIAM!
HAND OWER YER PURSE, WIFIE!
MY ARM'S SAIR! JINGS! AULD GRANNY GREENWAY'S BEIN' ROBBED!
I'LL SAVE YE, GRANNY!
THAT'S IT, WULLIE! BELT HIM ONE FOR ME!
CHEERIO, GRANNY!
'BYE, WULLIE! MIND AN' COME ROOND FOR TEA ON WEDNESDAY, NOW!
CRIVVENS! THON POT O' PAINT'LL HIT THAT WEE BOY!
GOT YE! YE WERE NEAR CLOBBERED THERE.
OUCH!
OH, YOU POOR BOY! IT'S LUCKY I WAS PASSING.HERE, LET ME HELP YOU!
A'BODY WILL WANT TAE HEAR MY STORY, NOW! IT'S BETTER THAN SOAPY'S OR FAT BOAB'S!
OH, WILLIAM! WHAT HAPPENED?
WELL, I SPRAINED MY WRIST RESCUIN' A PUIR WEE KITTEN FROM A TREE, THEN I GOT THUMPED SAVIN' GRANNY GREENWAY FROM A VICIOUS MUGGER . . .
. . . AND THEN I GOT KNOCKED OOT SAVIN' A WEE BOY FROM A FALLIN' POT O' PAINT! WHIT A HERO, EH?
HUH! YOU DON'T EXPECT US TO BELIEVE THAT, DO YOU?
AWA'! THON'S JIST A LOAD O' BLETHERS!
YE CANNA WIN!

*Whit a din! Whit a racket!—*

*And guess what's inside that big packet!*

HE'S AWA' DOON TOON
JOINER
HEY, WULLIE, COME OWER HERE! I'VE GOT A WEE JOB FOR YE!
TAK' THIS PARCEL DOON TAE THIS ADDRESS IN BLAIR STREET. HERE'S TWENTY PENCE TAE YERSEL'!
THANKS!
BLAIR STREET'S THE ITHER SIDE O' THE TOON! NEVER MIND, I CAN AYE AFFORD THE BUS, NOO!
OOPS!
OOF!
YE CLUMSY, TOUSLE-HEADED WEE TEARAWAY!
JINGS! WHIT A NOISE TAE MAK'!
PHEW! I'M SAFE, NOO!
HEY! WATCH WHIT YE'RE DAEIN', YE WEE SCOUNDREL!
SORRY, WIFIE, I'LL HELP YE PICK IT A' UP!
OUCH!
AARGH! I'VE SLIPPED ON A CAN!
EEK!
GEK YOUR FOOK OUK MY MOUF!
CRIVVENS! WHIT A DIN IN THERE!
CARRYIN' IT UP HERE SHOULD KEEP THIS THING OOT O' MISCHIEF!
HOI! WATCH OOT, SONNY!
YE'VE DONE IT, NOO!
GLOOB!
HELP M'BOAB!
IT'S A' YOUR FAULT!
IT WISNAE ME AT A'—IT WAS HIM!
WHIT A RACKET! I'M OFF!
AH, BLAIR STREET AT LAST! WHIT WAS THON NUMBER, AGAIN?
BLAIR ST.
AH, THAT'S IT!
DONG!
WATCH WHAUR YE'RE GOIN'! YE NEAR KNOCKED MY HEID AFF!
SORRY, MISTER! NAE NEED TAE SHOUT.
THIS IS IT. I'LL GET RID O' THIS PARCEL AT LAST!
31
OOPS! MIND OOT!
WOW!
SORRY, MISTER! YOU'RE NO' GOIN' TAE BAWL AT ME AN' A', ARE YE?
NO . . .
. . . YOUR PARCEL IS FOR US HERE AT THE LIBRARY.
SILENCE
WID YE BELIEVE IT?

*It seems Wull's scared o' Ba'heid but—*

*Oor lad soon shows that he's no mutt!*

HE'S AT A GANG MEETING.
I SAY WE CHOOSE A NEW GANG LEADER, AN' WULLIE'S NO' TAE GET THE JOB UNLESS HE FIGHTS BA'HEID BRAGG!
I SECOND THAT!
AN' I THIRD IT!
LATER—
WE'RE NO' WANTIN' YOU AS OOR LEADER UNLESS YE BEAT THON BULLY!
NOO'S YER CHANCE, WULLIE! HERE COMES BA'HEID!
JINGS! LOOK AT HIM GO! I'VE NEVER SEEN HIM RUN SO FAST!
YAH! COWARDIE-CUSTARD!
THIS IS NO' DAEIN' YER ELECTION CAMPAIGN MUCH GUID, YE KEN!
ACH, IT'S JIST MY NEW TACTICS!
PARK
I'LL GET YE, NOO, YE WEE NYAFF!
RUN!
HEY, YOU! GET AFF THON GRASS!
HUH! NOO WULLIE'S GETTIN' US INTAE TROUBLE, AN' A!
KEEP OFF THE GRASS
THIS MUST BE WHIT THEY CA' A RUNNIN' BATTLE.
AYE, BUT WITHOOT THE BATTLE!
YE'RE NO' MY HERO ANY MAIR, WULLIE!
ACH, I'M JIST WORKIN' OOT MY STRATEGY!
HAR-HAR!
HERE HE COMES AGAIN!
BEAT IT, LADS!
I'LL GET YE!
WULLIE'S TURNED CHICKEN!
MY WEE LEGS'LL NO' TAK' MUCH MAIR O' THIS!
HERE'S MY HOOSE! BA'HEID'LL NO' GET US IN THERE!
I'M NO' HIDIN' IN THERE! COME WI' ME, IF YE WANT TAE SEE BA'HEID GETTIN' CLOBBERED!
WHIT?
MAYBE HE'S PLANNIN' TAE EXHAUST BA'HEID AN' THEN FIGHT HIM!
BA'HEID'S NEVER EXHAUSTED! THEY SAY HE NEVER SLEEPS!
DINNA RUN DOON THERE, WULLIE! IT'S A DEAD END!
I KEN WHIT I'M DAEIN'!
HAR-HAR! I'VE GOT YE NOO, YE WEE SHRIMP!
HERE GOES!
TAK' THAT, BA'HEID!
I KENT A' ABOOT THON LOOSE PLANK! YE'VE GOT TAE HAE BRAINS TAE BE A LEADER, YE KEN!
HA-HA! THAT'S ME ELECTED FOR ANOTHER YEAR!

*The folk line up for Wull's coach trip—*

And sure enough, he gets a tip!

HULLO, MR WATSON! WHAUR ARE YE AFF TAE THE DAY?
I'M AWA' TAE TAK' A TOUR TAE GLEN BOGLE AN' LOCH FOWLIE.
THEN I'LL HAE MY DINNER AT THE DRUMMLY ARMS, AN' WHEN I GET HAME AGAIN MY PASSENGERS AYE TIP ME. IT'S A BRAW LIFE BEIN' A DRIVER!
HMM . . . THAT GIVES ME AN IDEA! CHEERIO, MR WATSON!
'BYE, WULLIE!
Wullie's Shed.
HAMMER! THUMP! BUMP!
A QUICK CONVERSION O' THE AULD CARTIE, AN' WE'RE A' SET!
WULLIE'S TOURS. ENJOY THE HERRYTAGE OF OOR TOON. 5P
THANK YOU, SIR! TAK' YER SEAT ON THE COACH, PLEASE.
THIS IS STOORIE BRAE, NAMED AFTER THE EARL O' STOORIE, WHA HELPED BONNIE PRINCE CHARLIE GIE THE VIKINGS A SKELPIN'!
I THOUGHT STOORIE BRAE WAS NAMED AFTER A' THE STOOR HERE!
IT'S A GUID JOB I'M HERE TAE KEEP YE RICHT, THEN!
GUST!
OVER THERE IS THE FAMOUS CRAGIE COLUMN, BUILT IN MEMORY O' SANDY CRAGIE, UNITED'S MANAGER WHEN THEY WON THE CUP.
HUH! SOME MONUMENT!
WE NOW COME TAE HILLSIDE ROAD, AN' PASSENGERS ARE REQUESTED TAE GET OOT AN' PUSH!
ON YER RIGHT IS THE QUARRY WHAUR RABBIE BURNS SERVED HIS TIME.
PECH!
WHEEZE!
NOW WE'LL JUST PULL OVER HERE FOR REFRESHMENTS AN' TAE LET YE STRETCH YER LEGS!
CAFE
YOU LOT HAE TAE BUY ME MY DINNER SEEIN' AS HOW I'M THE BUS DRIVER!
MENU
THAT WAS RARE! NOO IT'S BACK TAE THE DEPOT VIA HOGFIELD HOOSIN' SCHEME, A FINE EXAMPLE O' POST WAR GOTHIC ARCHIE-TEKTURE!
THIS IS THE SITE O' THE GREAT BATTLE O' HOGFIELD. AS YE CAN SEE, IT'S STILL GOIN' ON!
HAME AGAIN! WELL, I HOPE YE A' ENJOYED YER TOUR. BY THE WAY, THIS IS WHAUR YE TIP ME.
WE'LL TIP YE A' RIGHT!
ON TAE THE GROOND!
WAIT TILL I SEE THAT MR WATSON!

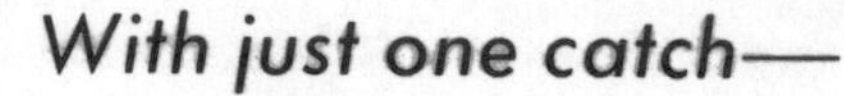
With just one catch—

*He's the man o' the match!*

WE'RE PLAYIN' MILL STREET SCHOOL AT FITBA' THE DAY.
SORRY, WULLIE. THE PITCH IS FLOODED, SO THE GEMME'S AFF. A' YER PALS ARE AWA' HAME.
THE HIGH SCHOOL PITCHES ARE A' RICHT. I'LL GO AN' WATCH THEM.
I SAY, SONNY, WE'RE A MAN SHORT FOR OUR GAME AGAINST FORGAN ACADEMY. WOULD YOU PLAY FOR US?
OKAY, MISTER!
COME ALONG! JUST JOIN IN THE GAME!
GREAT! MY FIRST TOUCH O' THE BA'!
HEY, REF! THIS BA'S BEEN PIT THROUGH A MANGLE! LOOK AT IT!
FOUL, REF!
ANIMALS! SEND THEM AFF, REF! DID YE SEE THAT?
HE JIST LAUGHED! MY, THEY'RE A RICHT ROUGH LOT FOR TOFFS!
HEY, REF, HANDBA'! WHAUR'S YER GUIDE DOG? YE MUST BE BLIND!
HUH! NAEBODY'S BOTHERIN' ABOOT THON FOUL!
OH, NO! WHIT A DUMPLIN'! AN OPEN GOAL, AN' HE PITS IT OWER THE BAR!
AWA'! IT'S A SKELP IN THE LUG HE NEEDS, NO' A PAT ON THE BACK!
LATER—
ACH, IT'S GOIN' OWER FOR A THROW-IN.
THAT BA'LL BE EVEN FLATTER IF I DINNA SAVE IT.
HURRAY!
GOT YE!
WELL DONE. THAT WAS A GREAT TRY.
WHIT DAE YE MEAN "TRY"? I SUCCEEDED!
WELL DONE, SONNY. YOUR THREE POINTS MEANS THAT THE HIGH SCHOOL WINS.
EH? BUT I NEVER GOT ANY GOALS.
HELP M'BOAB! NOO I'M MAN O' THE MATCH!
HOW WIS I TAE KEN THEY WERE PLAYIN' RUGBY?

# All Oor Wullie wants to know—

# Is what made Hen Broon grow and grow!

HE'S IN TROUBLE AGAIN!
I KEN FINE YE BROKE THON WINDIE, AN' IT WIS YOU THAT LET DOON THE TYRE ON MY BIKE, AN'...
NAG! NAG! NAG! AULD MOANER! WHEN I'M BIG I'LL JOIN THE POLIS AN' GET MY AIN BACK!
I'M OWER WEE FOR THE POLIS, THOUGH! I'VE GOT SOME GROWIN' TAE DAE!
THERE'S A BIG LAD! WONDER HOW HE GOT TAE BE THAT SIZE?
HEY, MISTER! HOW COME YOU'RE SO TALL?
THAT'S A GREAT SECRET, SONNY. POP IN HERE AN' I'LL SHOW YE!
GREAT! I KENT THERE WIS SOME SECRET WAY TAE GROW TALL!
HA-HA! THERE YE ARE—THE SECRET O' MY GREAT HEIGHT!
HUH!
THERE'S BERT McBURLY, THE SHOT-PUTTIN' CHAMP! HE MUST'VE BEEN BUYIN' THE FOOD THAT MAK'S HIM BIG.
GROC
HEY, BERT! IS THAT SOME MUSCLE-BUILDIN' GRUB YE'VE BEEN BUYIN'?
ER... NO' EXACTLY, WULLIE...
I'M ON SLIMMER'S FOOD. THE DOCTOR TOLD ME I WAS TOO BIG!
HERE'S THE MAN TAE ASK! HEN BROON MUST KEN A' ABOOT BEIN' TALL!
WHIT DID YE EAT AS A LADDIE, HEN?
NOTHIN' SPECIAL, WULLIE. CHOCOLATE, GRANNY SOOKERS, SUGAR MICE AN' THE ODD PLATE O' PORRIDGE.
PORRIDGE! I'D FORGOTTEN ABOOT THE PORRIDGE. THAT'S JIST WHAT I NEED!
GROCER
I THOUGHT HE'D PREFER THE GRANNY SOOKERS.
A WEEK LATER—
I'M WORRIED ABOOT WULLIE. THAT'S THE TENTH PACKET O' PORRIDGE HE'S BOUGHT THIS WEEK!
GROCER
HERE, WULLIE! DINNA GO EATIN' TOO MUCH PORRIDGE!
OCH, I'LL NO' NEED ANY MORE, NOO.
SOON—
THIS IS BRAW!
TAE THINK I OWE A' THIS TAE PORRIDGE.
I COLLECTED THE PACKET TOPS ON THE PORRIDGE AN' SENT FOR THIS MODEL VILLAGE!
I DIDNA GROW MUCH, BUT I HAD A BRAW TIME!

## *There's good reason for Wull's frowns—*

## *Life's got too many UPS and downs!*

HE'S AWA' TAE SEE HIS AUNT JEAN IN DRUMTOGLE.
HULLO, WULLIE! COME AWA' IN. IT'S GUID TAE SEE YE!
HULLO, AUNT JEAN.
I'VE GOT A WEE JOB FOR YOU AN' YER COUSIN WULLIE, JIM. THE DAY O' THE BOOLIN' CLUB'S NEXT MATCH HAS BEEN CHANGED, SO I WANT YE TAE DELIVER THESE NOTES TAE THE TEAM.
OKAY, DAD!
MAK' SURE YE HAND OWER THAE ENVELOPES PERSONALLY. DINNA GO STICKIN' THEM THROUGH LETTER-BOXES, THEY'RE URGENT!
THIS ANE'S FOR 23 K BURNSIDE COURT.
THAT'S BURNSIDE COURT. 23 K MUST BE RIGHT AT THE TOP!
ACH, THERE'LL BE A LIFT!
THERE'S A LIFT A' RICHT, BUT IT'S NO' WORKIN'!
OUT OF ORDER
WE'LL HAE TAE USE THE STAIRS!
...ONLY THREE MAIR FLAIRS TAE GO! GASP!
HERE YE ARE ... PECH ... MR McKAY ... WHEEZE!
THE NEXT ANE'S FOR DAVIE McLEOD.
THAT'LL SAVE US A WALK. THERE'S DAVIE UP THERE!
I'LL GO! I'M A GUID CLIMBER, AN' AULD MURDOCH'S NO' HERE TAE CHASE ME!
JINGS! THIS ISNAE SO EASY!
PECH! PECH! THERE YE ARE, MR McLEOD!
THANKS, SON!
PHEW! THON WIS HARD WORK AFTER A'!
LATER—
THE LAST ANE! SANDY GREIG, WHINCRAIG COTTAGE.
AW NO! I FORGOT— SANDY LIVES AT THE TOP O' A HILL!
IT'S STEEPER THAN IT LOOKS!
AYE! I'M FAIR PUGGLED!
PHEW! THIS IS FOR YOU, MR GREIG!
BACK HOME—
WE'VE GOT A WEE PROBLEM, BOYS. COME THROUGH TAE THE BEDROOM.
WHA'S CLIMBIN' UP TAE SLEEP ON THE TOP?
HIM!
I CANNA UNDERSTAND LADDIES NOOADAYS! I AYE WANTED TAE SLEEP ON THE TOP BUNK!
HE'S STILL SLEEPIN'! (AN' ON THE BOTTOM BUNK, SEEIN' HE WIS A GUEST!)

*Oor Wullie's smart. Trust him to find—*

*Auld comics of a different kind!*

MY AULD SHED'S JIST ABOOT FALLIN' DOON. IT'LL COST A FORTUNE TAE GET IT BACK INTAE SHAPE.
LATER—
HI, LADS! I'M GOIN' TAE RAISE MONEY TAE RESTORE MY SHED!
AWA'! YE COULDNA RAISE A SMILE!
SOON—
THEY'RE A' AWFY QUIET! WHIT'S GOIN' ON?
WHIT ARE YE DAEIN', WULLIE?
IT'S A SPONSORED SILENCE, MA . . . AW NO!
HA-HA! YE BROKE THE SILENCE, WULLIE!
TWA MINUTES, WULLIE! THAT'S HOW LANG YE STAYED QUIET!
"SOUNDS" LIKE YE'LL NO' BE MAKIN' MUCH MONEY THAT WAY, WULLIE! HA-HA!
SHORTLY—
GREAT! I'LL BRING MINE ROOND RICHT NOO!
CARS WASHED 20p
AHA! MY FIRST CUSTOMER!
HELP M'BOAB! LOOK AT THE SIZE O' THON CAR!
HMM . . . THAT WAS SUDDEN!
BIZNESS NOW CLOSED
I'LL JIST HAE TAE GET A RISE IN MY POCKET MONEY!
PA'S ALWAYS TELLIN' ME HOW TOUGH HE IS WI' HIS BOSS WHEN HE WANTS A RISE.
NOW LISTEN, PA! I NEED MAIR POCKET MONEY. WI' A' THIS INFLATION A'THING'S GOIN' SKY-HIGH . . .
. . . INCLUDIN' ME!
WHEECH!
GIVEN UP, HAVE YE, WULLIE?
NAW—HE'S STARTIN' ANOTHER SPONSORED SILENCE! HA-HA!
I'VE GOT IT! AULD COMICS! I'LL MAK' A PACKET!
MIND THE LAST TIME WULLIE TRIED SELLIN' AULD COMICS, SOAPY?
AYE, HE SOLD THE LOT . . .
CHEAT!
I'VE READ THIS ANE!
SWINDLER!
I WANT A REFUND!
. . . AN' ENDED UP MAKIN' A LOSS!
THAT AFTERNOON—
WHIT'S THAT? IT'S COMIN' FROM WULLIE'S BACK YARD!
HURRAY! HA! HA!
LET'S GO AN' SEE!
WHIT'S GOIN' ON, WULLIE?
OH, I MADE A PILE O' MONEY WI' THAE AULD COMICS . . .
HAVE YE FORGOTTEN ABOOT THON FIVER YE OWE ME?
NO' YET, GIE ME TIME!
GRANPAW BROON AN' SHUGGIE MACPHERSON ARE HELPIN' ME OOT! THEY'RE BRAW AULD COMICS!

*Oor lad provides big smiles all round—*

*Until Jacques' missing " pal " is found!*

HE'S PLAYIN' WI' HIS PALS . . .
THERE'S JACQUES, THON FRENCH LADDIE. HE LOOKS DOON IN THE DUMPS!
AYE, AN' THAT'S NO' SAE GUID WHEN YE'RE ON HOLIDAY!
I AM LONELY TODAY. THERE EEZ NO SIGN OF MY FRIEND BOBBY.
NEVER MIND, JACQUES, JIST COME AN' PLAY WI' US!
THIS IS WHAUR WE HIDE OOR FISHIN' GEAR, JACQUES!

DO YOU NOT HEED ZIS SIGN, WULLIE?
OH, AYE . . .
NO FISHING
. . . SOAPY AYE HANGS HIS JACKET ON IT!
WHAT EEZ ZAT NOISE?
CLATTER! CLANG!
IT'S TIME TAE GO!
THE GAMEY DIDNA SPOT OOR ALARM!
CLANG!
CLANG!
DINNA WORRY ABOOT THON SIGN EITHER, JACQUES!
MY, THIS IS BRAW!
KEEP OFF THE GRASS
AYE, THE SUNNIEST SPOT IN THE PARK!
THE PARK KEEPER! IT EEZ TIME TO GO AGAIN, YES?
NO' THIS TIME, JACQUES!
McTAVISH!
HEAD PARK KEEPER
B- BUT THERE'S LADDIES ON THE GRASS, BOSS!
HEE- HEE!
CHUCKLE!
BLETHERS! I KEN FINE YE WERE JIST TAKIN' A SHORT-CUT AGAIN!
I KNOW ZIS GAME, WULLIE! NOW WE RUN OFF, YES?
DRING!
NO—NOW WE STAY PUT!
YE CHEEKY WEE MONKEYS! I'LL GET YE!
GULP!
AAH!
HA- HA! NOW WE RUN, JACQUES!
SORRY, MISTER! JIST TYING MY SHOE- LACE!
THAT WIS BRAW, EH, JACQUES? YE CAN TELL YER PAL, BOBBY, WHIT FUN YE HAD!
AH, OUI! AND LOOK, HERE HE COMES NOW!
. . . AND THEY RANG ZIS DOORBELL, SO THE MAN WOULD COME OUT . . .
COME BACK HERE, YOU THREE!
PHEW! HA- HA! WHIT A LAUGH!

*Stand by for a funny sight—*

*When Oor Wull gets oot his kite!*

I'VE GOT A PENNY PURPLE, YE KEN!
STAMP ALBUM
ER . . . I HAD A PENNY PURPLE!
GUST!
HELP M'BOAB! IT'S STUCK TAE BIG CRUSHER BODIE!
PLOP!
I'LL JIST HAE TAE ASK HIM FOR IT!
WHIT DAE YE WANT?
A STAMP, PLEASE.
THERE YE ARE THEN!
STAMP!
WHIT DAE YE WANT?
ER . . . NOTHIN' REALLY.
HUH! ROTTEN WIND!
THIS WIND'S BRAW FOR MY KITE, THOUGH!
WHOOSH!
JINGS! THE WIND'S CAUGHT MY KITE!
GASHP! MY TEESH!
I'D BETTER MAK' A QUICK GETAWAY THROUGH THON GATE!
ROAR!
SLAM!
OOF! IT'S BLOWN SHUT!
ISH A PEESH O' NONSHENSH PLAYIN' WI' KISHE SHAE CLOSHE TAE HOOSHESH!
WISH I KENT WHIT HE WIS SAYIN'!
HUMPH! I'M FED UP O' THIS WIND!
OUCH!
WHEEECH!
I'VE HAD ENOUGH O' A'THING BLOWIN' ABOOT FOR ONE DAY! I'M GOIN' INDOORS!
HMM . . . MAYBE I SPOKE TOO SOON!
AYE, YE NEED PLENTY O' WIND FOR BLAW FITBA'!

*Here's the smartest—*

*Comic artist!*

MY, IT'S A BRAW DAY.
HEY, WULLIE! I'LL GIE YE FIFTY PENCE IF YE WHITEWASH MY WALL!
OKAY, MR FLEMMING! YE'RE ON!
I'D DAE IT MASEL', BUT I'VE GOT SOME WORK TAE DAE IN THE GARDEN.
I'LL HAE SOME FUN AFORE I START!
HA-HA! A MASTER-PIECE!
P.C. MURDOCH HAS BIG FEET, LIKE TWA BOATS IN THE FISHING FLEET.
YE'LL GET TOKIO FOR PAINTIN' ON THON WALL, WULLIE!
NA, NA! I'M A'RICHT!
LET'S TRY AGAIN!
BRILLIANT!
YE'LL BE IN BIG TROUBLE FOR WRITIN' ON THAT WALL, WULLIE.
HA-HA! DINNA WORRY. I'LL NO' GET INTAE TROUBLE!
NOSEY NISBET OOR TEECHER
IN FACT, THE MAIR PAINTIN' I DAE, THE BETTER!
WHIT'S THAT?
WAIT AN' SEE!
HA-HA-HA!
GREAT LIKENESS, EH?
I AM A WORM LIKE SPECKY SIMBSOM
THAT'S AWFY GUID, WULLIE, BUT YE'LL CATCH IT IF ANYONE SEES YE.
ACH, I'M NO BOTHERED. YE CANNA SCARE ME!
HERE'S AULD FLEMMING! YE'RE FOR IT NOW, WULLIE!
HOW ARE YOU GETTIN' ON, WULLIE?
HA-HA! AYE, VERY FUNNY, WULLIE, BUT THERE'S JIST ONE THING—THIS IS NO' MY WALL . . .
. . . THAT'S MINE OWER THERE. THIS ANE'S THE HEADMASTER'S. I'M JUST DAEIN' HIS GARDENIN'!
YE'D BETTER COVER UP A' THIS LOT AFORE YE START ON MY BIT!
ACH, BELT UP, YOU LOT! I'LL BE HERE TILL BED TIME NOW!
IT'S ENOUGH TAE DRIVE YE UP THE WA'!

*Nae wonder Wullie's feelin' grim—*

*Guess who's played a trick on HIM!*

PARCEL FOR YOU, WULLIE.
OH, BOY!
G.P.O.
JINGS! LOOK AT THIS! UNCLE TAM'S SENT ME A PRACTICAL JOKE SET!
PRACTICAL JOKE SET.
HUMPH! THERE'LL BE NAE END O' TROUBLE WI' THAT!
WHIT'S THAT AWFY SMELL?
YE WEE MONKEY! YOU'VE LET AFF A STINK BOMB, HAVEN'T YE?
NO' ME, MA.
SORRY ABOOT THE SMELL, MISSUS. THERE'S A BURST GAS MAIN OOTSIDE YER HOOSE. WE'RE FIXIN' IT NOW.
OH, MY. I'M SORRY, WULLIE.
I WAS WRONG ABOOT WULLIE. MAYBE HE'LL NO' BE A NUISANCE WI' THAT JOKE SET.
GASP! I SPOKE TOO SOON! HE'S HAD PA USIN' BLACKFACE SOAP!
BLACKFACE SOAP! SO THAT'S YER GAME!
EH?
GOT A RAG, MA? I'M A' COVERED IN OIL. I'VE BEEN MENDIN' THE CAR.
OH—ER—AYE. AWA' AN' PLAY, WULLIE.
LATER—
LOOK WHIT I FOUND IN THE LIVIN' ROOM, MA!
HUH! YE CANNA FOOL ME WI' A PLASTIC SPIDER!
I'M NO' KIDDIN'. IT'S REAL. I'M TAKIN' IT OOTSIDE.
EEK!
GET THAT HORRIBLE THING OOT O' HERE!
WULLIE!
I SAW YE PUTTIN' A TRICK BISCUIT ON THAT PLATE!
NO, MA. I WIS GOIN' TAE PINCH ANE, BUT I DECIDED TAE PUT IT BACK. STILL, TAE PROVE MY INNOCENCE . . .
. . . I'D BETTER EAT IT!
I THOUGHT IT WAS A TRICK OOT O' THON BOX! I'VE BEEN AWFY TAE YE THIS MORNIN', WULLIE. I'M SORRY.
TAE TELL YE THE TRUTH, MA, I'VE NO' BEEN ABLE TAE GET THE LID AFF THE BOX!
AYE, WULLIE, YE'RE NO' THE ONLY JOKER IN THE HOOSE! I GLUED DOWN THE LID O' YER BOX!
HUH! I CANNA STAND PRACTICAL JOKERS!

*Wull's paintings may well be disasters—*

*But they all sell, just like Old Masters!*

BELIEVE IT OR NOT—HE'S AT THE ART GALLERY!
MODERN ART SECTION.
HELP M'BOAB! WHIT A LOAD O' JUNK!
A "LOAD OF JUNK" IS IT? I'LL HAVE YOU KNOW THAT JUNK IS WORTH THOUSANDS OF POUNDS, YOUNG MAN.
ART SECTION
WORTH THOUSANDS, EH? I COULD DAE BETTER MASEL'! NOW THERE'S AN IDEA . . .
ART GALLERY
I'LL MAK' A FORTUNE! FOLK WILL BE QUEUEIN' UP TAE BUY A GENUINE ORIGINAL OOR WULLIE MASTERPIECE!
Wullie's Shed
I'LL TRY A LANDSCAPE FIRST OF ALL.
IT'S EASY ONCE YE'RE STARTED.
HULLO, HEN!
GET AFF O' THERE!
BEAT IT, YOU!
JINGS!
LOOK AT THE MESS YE'VE CAUSED, YE WEE RASCAL!
I'M OFF!
HUMPH! I'LL HAE TAE START AGAIN, NOW!
WHIT ON EARTH . . ?
OINK! OINK!
WOW!
YE'VE TURNED MY BONNY LANDSCAPE INTAE A PROPER PIG'S BREAKFAST!
OINK!
THIS ANE'S BRAW! IT'S NEARLY FINISHED, NOW.
HONK!
YIKES!
HELLO, WULLIE. ARE YER PAINTIN'S FOR SALE?
AYE, BUT THEY'RE A' RUINED BY YER ANIMALS, THOUGH!
I'LL GIE YE A POUND FOR THE LOT!
DONE!
JINGS! JIST THINK WHIT I'LL GET FOR ANES IN GUID CONDITION!
HE MUST BE AWA' TAE HANG THEM IN HIS BIG HOOSE. MAYBE HE HAS HIS AIN WEE GALLERY. I'LL GO AN' SEE!
AW, NO!
THIS'LL STOP A' THE ANIMALS GETTIN' OOT O' THE FARMYARD AN' SPOILIN' YER PAINTIN'S, WULLIE!
I'LL BET NAEBODY EVER MENDED A FENCE WI' THE MOANIN' LISA!

*Oor Wullie comes a proper cropper—*

*His essay sounds like one big " whopper "!*

HE'S AT SCHOOL.
I WANT YOU ALL TO WRITE AN ESSAY TONIGHT. KEEP IT NICE AND SIMPLE. WRITE ABOUT THINGS WHICH HAPPEN TO YOU EVERY DAY.
WE'LL NO' SEE YE THE NICHT, WULLIE, SEEIN' AS HOW WE'VE GOT THON ESSAY TAE WRITE.
SCHOOL
AYE, A'RICHT THEN.
JINGS! LOOK AT THON GORILLA! IT'S LIKE A CROSS BETWEEN MASHER Mc TURK AN' FAT BOAB!
MUSEUM
SNAP!
MICHTY ME! THE ROPE'S SNAPPED!
HELP M'BOAB, HE NEAR GOT ME! MAYBE I SHOULDN'T HAVE INSULTED HIM!
SORRY, WULLIE! ARE YE OKAY?
ME? OCH, AYE— I'M TOUGH AS NAILS (PHEW!)
LOOK AT THIS! IT MUST BE THE START O' THE DRUMTOGLE FESTIVAL!
HEY, WULLIE! COMIN' FOR A HURL IN MY HYPER-SPACE ASTRAL CRUISER?
SPACE TREK.
SURE, MR SMITH!
WAHEY! THIS IS BRAW!
'BYE, WULLIE!
CHEERIO, MR SMITH, AN' THANKS!
A WEDDIN'! WONDER IF THERE'LL BE A SCRAMMIE? JINGS, LOOK AT THAT!
MADE IT! THON LASSIE WOULD'VE SPOILED THE TRAIN O' THE BRIDE'S BONNY DRESS!
THANK YOU, WILLIAM. THAT WAS A VERY KIND AND THOUGHTFUL THING TO DO!
ACH, IT WAS NOTHIN'!
HOME AT LAST—
ACH, WELL, I'D BETTER DAE MY HAMEWORK, I SUPPOSE!
NEXT MORNING—
ALL RIGHT, HAND IN YOUR ESSAYS, PLEASE!
LATER—
WILLIAM! I TOLD EVERYONE TO WRITE A NICE, SIMPLE ESSAY ABOUT EVERYDAY THINGS! WHAT'S THIS YOU'VE WRITTEN?
" . . . ON MY WAY HOME I HAD TO JUMP OUT OF THE WAY OF A FALLING GORILLA. THEN I GOT A LIFT IN A HYPER-SPACE ASTRAL CRUISER, AND LATER SAVED A TRAIN FROM BEING RUN OVER BY A GIRL ON ROLLER SKATES!"
NAEBODY WOULD BELIEVE IT WAS A' TRUE!

All Wullie's ploys go sadly wrong—

Until his uncle comes along.

THINK I'LL GO OOT ON MY CARTIE THE DAY.
MAN, I'M DAEIN' SOME SPEED!
OW 1
HELP M'BOAB! AN EARTHQUAKE!
OW 1
GULP!
HERE, WHIT'S GOIN' ON?
SORRY, WULLIE. I'M FIXIN' THE UNDERGROUND TELEPHONE CABLE DOON HERE.
YE SHOULD BE MAIR CAREFUL THEN! WHIT IF I'D BEEN A STEAM ROLLER?
OW 1
ACH, WELL, IT WIS NEEDIN' A SERVICE, ANYWAY. I'LL HAE A GEMME O' FITBA.
THERE'S PLENTY O' ROOM TAE HAE A KICK ABOOT DOON AT THE PARK.
AW, NO!
IT'S THE MOLES THAT DAE THIS, WULLIE. YE CANNA CATCH THEM, EITHER. THEY'RE AYE UNDERGROUND.
MAIR UNDER-GROUND TROUBLE!
I'LL SAIL MY BOAT IN STOORIE BURN.
LOOK AT IT GO! IT'S THE BEST WEE RACER THIS SIDE O' AUCHEN-TOGLE!
HEY! WHAUR'S THE BURN GONE?
DID YE NO' KEN, WULLIE? THE BURN'S BEEN PIPED UNDERGROUND TAE MAK' WAY FOR THON NEW HOOSIN' SCHEME!
THIS IS AWFY! UNDERGROUND MENACES ARE SPOILIN' A' MY FUN!
I'LL DAE A SPOT O' FISHIN' TAE CHEER MASEL' UP.
MY FISHIN' LINE'S IN HERE SOMEWHERE.
NA IT'S NO! MY DOG FOUND YER FISHIN' LINE, WULLIE. HE HAULED IT OOT AN'...
DINNA TELL ME —HE BURIED IT!
RIGHT FIRST TIME!
LATER—
CHEER UP, WULLIE. YER UNCLE JOCK'S HERE. HE'S GOT A SPECIAL TREAT FOR YE!
I'M A TRAIN DRIVER, WULLIE. COME WI' ME AN' I'LL TAK' YE FOR A HURL IN MY TRAIN.
WILL WE GO OWER BRIDGES, THROUGH FIELDS, AN' THE LIKE?
NO, WULLIE. I DRIVE A TRAIN ON AN UNDERGROUND LINE!
SWOON!
I WENT, ANYWAY. IT WAS BRAW!

*Oor Wullie's life is never borin'—*

*Here he is, awa' explorin'!*

HE'S WATCHIN' TV.
THIS IS A BRAW PROGRAMME ABOOT DAVID NATTERBOROUGH, THE EXPLORER.
. . . AND THIS IS THE BEELA-BEELA MONKEY.
JINGS, THON LAD WENT TAE BONGOLAND AN' DISCOVERED A RIVER, AN UNKNOWN TRIBE O' INDIANS, A NEW KIND O' BOAR, AN' A LOST CITY!
THINK I'LL AWA' AN' DAE SOME EXPLORIN', MASEL'!
I'VE DISCOVERED SOMETHIN' ALREADY. THERE'S A NEW, UNCHARTED RIVER!
ACH, IT'S JIST MR SIMPSON'S AULD BANGER!
I'LL HEAD UP TOWARDS THE PARK.
HELLO, WHIT'S THAT? SOUNDS LIKE FOREIGN VOICES!
CHATTER!
THERE MUST BE A LOST TRIBE HIDIN' OOT IN THE PARK! I'LL NIP ALONG THIS BRANCH TAE SPOT THEM.
HUMPH! IT'S JIST MR PATEL, THE GROCER, OOT FOR A WALK WI' HIS BAIRNS!
THE BRAVE EXPLORER SET OOT AGAIN ON HIS DANGEROUS JOURNEY . . .
. . . SUDDENLY A TERRIBLE SOUND WAS HEARD! COULD IT BE A NEW TYPE O' BOAR?
GRUNT! SNORT!
NA! IT'S JIST AN OLD TYPE O' BORE—GRAN'PAW BROON!
NODDING OFF!
NODDED OFF!
. . . THEN AFTER I CAPTURED THE KAISER . . .
ACH, I'LL NEVER DISCOVER ANYTHIN' WORTHWHILE.
BUT WHIT WIS THAT? SOMETHIN' MOVIN' IN THE LONG GRASS! LIONS? TIGERS?
RUSTLE!
IT'S A WEE CAT! HELLO THERE, PUSSY.
I SEE FROM YER COLLAR TAG YE'RE A LANG WAY FROM HAME. MAYBE I SHOULD TAK' YE BACK.
SO—
OH, THANKS EVER SO MUCH. WE THOUGHT WE'D NEVER SEE POOR KITTY AGAIN. PLEASE, TAKE THIS FIFTY PENCE AS A REWARD.
JINGS! THANKS, MISSUS!
ACH, WELL. I DIDNA FIND A LOST CITY, JIST A LOST KITTY, BUT I BET I WAS BETTER PAID THAN THON TV LAD!

*Pets are troublesome, no' half—*

*Just see Wull's " enormouse " laugh!*

BET YE WISH YE HAD A DOG, WULLIE.
I'VE NAE TIME FOR TROUBLESOME ANIMALS.
REMEMBER WHEN YE WERE TRAININ' YER HOUND . . .
HE BROUGHT THE STICK BACK A'RICHT . . .
BUT IT WIS THE PARKIE'S LITTER-COLLECTIN' STICK!
THON PARKIE'S A TERROR WHEN HE'S ANGRY. YE CAN KEEP YER DOG.
I'VE GOT ANOTHER FISH FOR MY BOWL, WULLIE. BRAW, EH?
I THOUGHT YE'D GIVEN UP KEEPIN' THAE DANGEROUS PETS!
DANGEROUS? IT'S JIST A WEE FISH!
WHIT? HAVE YE FORGOTTEN THE TIME WHEN . . .
. . . THON BOWL SLIPPED OOT YER HANDS? YE COULDNAE PLAY FITBA' FOR WEEKS.
MIND YOU, YOU COULD NEVER PLAY FITBA', ANYWAY! HA-HA! SOME PETS ARE AN AWFY PROBLEM.
TIGER'S A BONNY CAT, EH, WULLIE?
DAE YE NO' MIND THE TIME IT DISAPPEARED UNDER YER GARDEN SHED, ECK?
HE CAME OOT BY HIMSEL' EASILY ENOUGH!
AYE, BUT YOU DIDNA!
IT TOOK TWA FIREMEN TAE GET YOU OOT!
I CANNA UNDERSTAND FOWK KEEPIN' TROUBLE-SOME PETS! THEY'RE A' DAFT!
SO THERE YE ARE! WE'VE BEEN TALKIN' TAE P.C. MURDOCH! TWA BROKEN WINDAES THIS WEEK!
GET STRAIGHT TAE BED, MY LAD! NAE SUPPER FOR YOU!
I'LL HAVE TAE SNEAK DOON FOR SOMETHIN' TAE EAT LATER! I'M STARVIN'!
LATER—
QUIETLY DOES IT! MA AN' PA WILL BE ASLEEP BY NOW!
I'LL JIST HAE A FEW BISCUITS. BETTER WATCH THIS SQUEAKY DOOR!
OOH—HA-HA-HA! HA-HA-HA!
WHIT'S GOIN' ON?
HEE-HEE! HA-HA!
JEEMY! YE NEAR TICKLED ME TAE DEATH!
I CAUGHT HIM RAIDIN' THE LARDER, MA!
TRAITOR!
WID YE BELIEVE IT? EVEN JEEMY'S A TROUBLESOME PET!

*Michty me, just tak' a look—*

*Here's Wull the waiter, Bob the cook!*

POSH NOSH
IL MUNCHERAMA
JINGS! LOOK AT THAT POSH LAD COMIN' OOT O' THON FANCY RESTAURANT.
THAT WIS TONI MACARONI, WULLIE. HE MAK'S A FORTUNE IN THON RESTAURANT O' HIS.
REALLY?
COME ON, BOAB. WE'RE GOIN' TAE GET RICH, AN' A'! WE'LL OPEN A RESTAURANT!
THAT'S THE TABLE SET, BOAB. READY TO OPEN?
READY WHEN YOU ARE, WULLIE!
SAY, THIS LITTLE PLACE LOOKS REAL CUTE!
HIGH CLASS
CAFE
INTERNATIONAL
COOKIN'
LET'S TRY IT, ELMER!
THIS IS OOR BEST TABLE— THERE'S NAE NAILS STICKIN' OOT O' IT!
REAL SWELL, AIN'T IT, AMY?
WE'LL HAVE PRAWN COCKTAIL, VICHYSSOISE AND FRESH LOBSTER WITH BERNAISE SAUCE.
TWA LENTIL SOUPS AN' A COUPLE O' BRIDIES, BOAB!
COMIN' RIGHT UP, WULLIE.
WULLIE! I CANNA GET THE PRIMUS STOVE TAE LIGHT.
WE'VE GOT FOWK WAITIN', AN' A'! I'LL SEE WHAT MA'S COOKIN'!
I'LL TAK' THIS POT. IT'S BOUND TAE BE GUID.
WE'RE RICHT OOT O' WHATEVER IT WIS YE ORDERED. TRY THIS TRADITIONAL SCOTTISH DISH INSTEAD.
HANKIES?
CRIVVENS! TRUST ME TAE PICK THE POT MA WIS BILIN' THE HANKIES IN! ER—I'LL BE BACK IN A MINUTE, SIR!
QUICK, BOAB, NIP ACROSS TAE JOCK'S MOBILE CHIPPER FOR TWA PUDDEN SUPPERS.
JOCK'S
AHEM! OOR CHEF IS JIST PUTTIN' THE FINISHIN' TOUCHES TAE YER MEAL.
. . . AN' HERE HE COMES, NOO!
I TOLD YE THON APRON WIS OWER BIG FOR YE, BOAB!
OOPS!
TRIP!
GAWSH!
YOU SHOULD CALL THE COPS, ELMER. THIS IS JUST TERRIBLE!
HUH! OOR RESTAURANT MADE A LOSS O' EIGHTY SIX PENCE FOR THE PUDDEN SUPPERS!

*Oor Wullie's shopping list's so long—*

*He's guaranteed to get it wrong!*

THINK AH'LL GO FOR A STROLL DOON THE TOON.
EVENTIDE HOME
C'MERE A WEE MINUTE, WULLIE.
COULD YOU NIP DOON TAE TONI'S AN' GET A MESSAGE—THREE FISH SUPPERS WI' BROON SAUCE, TWA RED PUDDIN' SUPPERS WI' SALT BUT NAE VINEGAR, FOWER HAGGIS, ANE WI' A PICKLED ONION, AN' A POKE O' CHIPS AN' PEAS.
OKAY!
NOW WHIT WIZ THAT AGAIN—SIX HAGGIS SUPPERS WI'BROON PEAS . . . NA, THAT'S NO' RICHT.
AH'D BETTER WRITE IT DOON AN' MEMORISE IT.
CHIPS
I'LL WASH DOON MY STEP . . .
JINGS! SORRY, WULLIE! AH DIDNA SEE YE BENDIN' DOON THERE. COME IN AN' GET DRIED.
IT'S OKAY—JIST GIE ME A WEE BIT PAPER.
YE'LL NEVER DRY YERSEL' WI' THAT.
AH MIND NOW—FOWER SINGLE HAGGIS, ANE WI' A PICKLED RED PUDDIN' . . .
HELP MA BOAB!
BALLET SCHOOL
THAT'S A 'BALLET' NUISANCE! AH CANNA GO IN THERE AFTER IT!
AH KEN. AH'LL WRITE DOON THE LIST ON MA HAND. THAT'LL NO' BLOW AWA'. TWA PIE SUPPERS WI' A HELPIN' O' FISH . . .
THAT'S IT, NOO!
JINGS—HERE'S THE MEENISTER!
NICE TO MEET YOU, WILLIAM!
IT'S A' SMUDGED! IT'LL JIST HAE TAE BE MEMORY NOO.
AH'VE GOT AN ORDER FOR YE FRAE THE OLD FOLKS' HOME . . .
CHIPS & HAGGIS
CHIPS & PUDDING
LATER.
THERE YE ARE!
THANKS!
THAT'S EXACTLY WHAT WE ORDERED—HOW DID YE DAE IT?
ACH, IT WAS NAE TROUBLE!
READER'S VOICE
THAT'S AMAZIN'—HE DIDNAE HAE A CLUE!
FOOLED YE A'! TONI SAID THEY'D BEEN GETTIN' THE SAME ORDER FUR THE LAST TEN YEARS.

*Here's a special snowball fight—*

*Trust oor lad to do things " write "!*

YIPPEE! LOOK AT A' THIS SNA'!
I'LL NEED PLENTY SNA' BA'S.
THERE, THAT SHOULD DAE.
WULLIE'S A' READY FOR A SNA' BA' FIGHT. I'LL SURPRISE HIM.
BULL'S EYE!
YEUCH!
AWA' YE GO, ECK. I'M HEADIN' FOR P.C. MURDOCH'S PLACE.
HI, WULLIE! HOW ABOOT A SNA' BA' FIGHT?
SORRY, LADS! I'LL BE NEEDIN' A' THESE ROOND AT P.C. MURDOCH'S HOOSE.
HE'S DAFTER THAN WE THOUGHT! WE MUST SEE THIS!
WELLA HELLO, WULLIE. YOU FANCY HOT DRINK TODAY, YES?
TONI'S SWEET SHOP
NO, THE DAY, TONI. I'VE GOT IMPORTANT BUSINESS ROOND AT P.C. MURDOCH'S HOOSE.
THAT'S RICHT. HE SAYS A' THOSE SNA' BA'S ARE FOR MURDOCH!
SMASHIN'! I'VE BEEN LOOKIN' FORWARD TAE THIS A' YEAR!
P.C. MURDOCH
HA-HA! BANG ON TARGET.
AND ANOTHER ONE!
BRILLIANT SHOT!
NEXT ANE COMIN' UP!
THERE! THAT'S IT FINISHED!
MERRY CHRISTMAS A'body
NO' BAD, EH?
P.C. MURDOCH'S GOT THE LANGEST FENCE IN TOON IT WIS JUST WHIT I NEEDED!

## See that big smile on Ma's face—

## She's got the perfect hiding-place!

JINGS! SMELL THAT! MA'S MAKIN' TABLET!
MMM . . . GREAT! I'LL HAVE TAE GET SOME O' THAT!
GET YER BEADY EYES AFF THAT TABLET, WULLIE. YER PA'S TAKIN' IT DOON TAE THE BOOLIN' CLUB. THEY'RE GETIN' A' THING READY FOR THEIR HOGMANAY PARTY.
I DINNA WANT YOU MEDDLIN' WI' THIS. I'M PUTTIN' IT AWA' TAE COOL.
HEE-HEE! I'M OWER SMART FOR MA! I'LL SOON FIND WHAUR SHE'S LEFT IT.
THIS IS ANE O' HER FAVOURITE HIDIN' PLACES.
SURE ENOUGH! HERE'S THE TABLET!
WULLIE!
MA! WHIT A FLEG YE GAVE ME!
SHE'S GONE AN' HIDDEN IT SOMEWHERE ELSE, NOO!
HA-HA! FOUND IT! THAT DIDNA TAK' LANG!
YE WEE MONKEY! DON'T YOU DARE TOUCH THAT!
GULP! NABBED AGAIN!
IT'S JIST ABOOT READY FOR CUTTIN' UP, NOO.
ACH, MA! I ONLY WANT A WEE BIT!
AWA' YE GO AN' GET ON WI' YER HAMEWORK.
HAMEWORK? NAE CHANCE! I'D RATHER WATCH YOU!
THAT'S ANOTHER BAGFUL. I SHOULD HAE JIST ENOUGH LEFT TAE FILL ONE MAIR BAG.
OR MY PUIR EMPTY TUMMY.
GET AWA'! IT'S NO'LANG SINCE YE HAD YER DINNER. WHY DON'T YE DAE YER HAMEWORK? YE'VE GOT GEOGRAPHY AN' SUMS TAE DAE.
I'LL DAE MY HAMEWORK ONCE I'VE FOUND WHAUR SHE'S GOING TAE HIDE THAT TABLET!
IT'S NO' THERE.
AN' IT'S NO' IN THE SIDEBOARD.
NO' UP THE LUM, EITHER.
I'M AWA' DOON TAE THE BOOLIN' CLUB NOO, MA. CAN YE GIVE ME THAT TABLET YE MADE?
AYE.
I HID IT IN WULLIE'S SCHOOLBAG. HE WIS GIVEN HAMEWORK TAE DAE OWER THE HOLIDAYS, AN' I KENT HE WID NEVER GO NEAR THE BOOKS IN HIS BAG.
I'M MAKIN' A NEW YEAR RESOLUTION TAE AYE DAE MY HAMEWORK AS SOON AS POSSIBLE!

# Eyewitness
# CHRISTIANITY

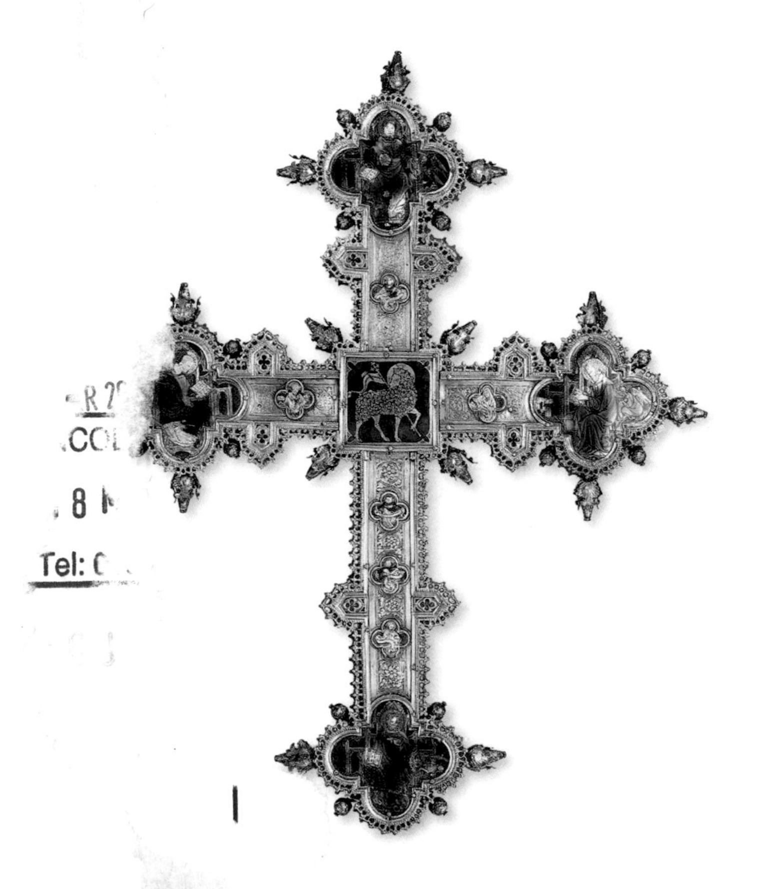

Russian Orthodox icons

Salvation Army song leader playing a cornet

Abbot's crozier

Holy water stoup

Stained-glass fragment depicting the Madonna and Child

Horn of Saint Hubert

Model of the *Mayflower*

# Eyewitness CHRISTIANITY

Written by
PHILIP WILKINSON

Photographed by
STEVE TEAGUE

Illuminated Latin psalter

DK

LONDON, NEW YORK, MELBOURNE,
MUNICH, and DELHI

**For Bookwork Ltd**
**Editor** Annabel Blackledge
**Art editor** Kate Mullins

**For DK Publishing**
**Managing editor**
Andrew Macintyre
**Managing art editors**
Clare Shedden, Jane Thomas
**US editors** Margaret Parrish, Christine Heilman
**Category publisher** Linda Martin
**Production controller** Erica Rosen
**Picture researchers**
Angela Anderson, Bridget Tily
**Picture librarian** Claire Bowers
**DTP designer** Siu Yin Ho
**Jacket designer** Dean Price

**Consultants**
Annette Reynolds,
AD Publishing Services Ltd,
Jon Reynolds, Diocesan Director of Education

**PAPERBACK EDITION**
**Editor** John Searcy
**Writer** Elizabeth Hester
**Consultant** Peggy Morgan
**Publishing director** Beth Sutinis
**Senior designer** Tai Blanche
**Designer** Diana Catherines
**Photo research** Chrissy McIntyre
**Art director** Dirk Kaufman
**DTP designer** Kathy Farias
**Production** Ivor Parker

This Eyewitness ® Guide has been conceived by
Dorling Kindersley Limited and Editions Gallimard

Hardback edition first published in Great Britain in 2003
This edition first published in Great Britain in 2006 by
Dorling Kindersley Limited,
80 Strand, London WC2R 0RL

2 4 6 8 10 9 7 5 3 1



A CIP catalogue record for this book
is available from the British Library.

ISBN-13: 978-1-40531-603-3
ISBN-10: 1-4053-1603-9

Colour reproduction by
Colourscan, Singapore
Printed in China by
Toppan Co. (Shenzen) Ltd.

# Contents

Abbot in ceremonial robes

# In the beginning

THE BIBLE BEGINS WITH stories of the creation of the world and the early Jewish people. These books, which make up the Old Testament of the Christian Bible, and which are also sacred to the Jews, were written by Jewish scribes long before the birth of Jesus. For the Jews they are important because they describe the covenant, or special relationship, between God and the Jewish people. For Christians the Old Testament has added significance because many of the stories seem to prefigure, or mirror, events that happened later when Jesus came to save humankind from sin.

4th-century depiction of Adam and Eve in Eden

**FORBIDDEN FRUIT**
Genesis, the first book of the Bible (p. 20), tells how God created Heaven and Earth, land and water, animals and birds, and finally Adam and Eve – the first man and woman. God put them in the Garden of Eden, and told them that the only fruit they must not eat was the fruit of the Tree of Knowledge.

**ENEMY IN EDEN**
Satan, who lived in Hell (pp. 26–27), was God's archenemy. Early Jewish writers said that the serpent in the Garden of Eden, a cunning tempter, was Satan in disguise. In the Book of Genesis, the serpent tempts Eve to eat the forbidden fruit, just as Satan later tempted Jesus in the New Testament.

This 12th-century painting of Satan shows him with Saint Michael

*Saint Michael is weighing souls to determine whether they should go to Heaven or Hell*

*Satan*

The serpent is often pictured as a snake like this red spitting cobra

The forbidden fruit is often imagined to have been an apple

**ORIGINAL SIN**
The serpent tempted Eve to eat the forbidden fruit, and Adam followed suit. God was angry at their disobedience and threw them out of the Garden of Eden. Christians believe that Adam and Eve, and their descendants, were tainted with this "original sin". Only the coming of Jesus Christ would eventually offer humankind a way of escaping sin and achieving everlasting life with God.

*The dove brought Noah a leaf to show that the flood waters were going down*

Mosaic of Noah and his family in the ark

**THE GREAT FLOOD**
Another story in Genesis tells how God became disenchanted with all the evil in the world, and sent a great flood to destroy much of the wickedness. Only one good man, Noah, was allowed to escape with his family. He built a great boat, the ark, in which he, his sons and their wives, and all the birds and animals took refuge. Christians think of Noah as the second father of the human race, after Adam.

> *"Don't hurt the boy or do anything to him. Now I know that you honour and obey God."*
>
> GENESIS 22:12
> Angel of the Lord to Abraham

God provided a ram for Abraham's sacrifice

**SACRIFICIAL RAM**
God ordered Abraham to kill his son Isaac as a sacrifice. Abraham was about to obey when an angel told him to stop and kill a ram instead. Christians see this story as a prophecy of the way in which God would sacrifice Jesus.

Daniel window from Augsburg Cathedral in Germany

Isaiah window from Augsburg Cathedral in Germany

Moses window from Augsburg Cathedral in Germany

**PROPHETS AND LEADERS**
The Old Testament contains stories about Jewish ancestors such as Abraham and the great leader Moses, who guided the Jews from slavery in Egypt back to their homeland. The Old Testament also includes writings about and by prophets such as Isaiah and Daniel, who told of the coming of a Messiah, or saviour.

# The birth of Jesus

**HUMBLE BEGINNINGS**
Mary and Joseph were staying in Bethlehem at the time of the nativity, or birth, of Jesus. All the inns in the town were full, so Jesus had to be born in the humblest of surroundings – a stable.

THE GOSPELS (p. 21) tell how a virgin called Mary gave birth to Jesus Christ in Bethlehem. Followers of Christ (Christians) believe that Jesus was God's son, and that the prophets of the Old Testament had predicted he would come and save humankind from sin. The idea that God became human in this way is called the incarnation, meaning that God's spirit was made into human flesh. The birth of Jesus marked the origin of the Christian religion.

*Mary is traditionally shown wearing blue*

**MADONNA AND CHILD**
Statues of Mary, or the Madonna, and the infant Jesus are a reminder of Mary's vital role in the Christian story. She is a link between the human and spiritual worlds.

*The angels play instruments that were popular in the 16th century, when this altarpiece was made*

*The Holy Spirit is shown in the form of a dove*

Modern mosaic from Old Plaza Church in California, USA

**THE ANNUNCIATION**
Luke's Gospel describes how the angel Gabriel appeared to Mary to tell her that, even though she was a virgin, she was about to become pregnant. Gabriel announced that Mary would be visited by the Holy Spirit (p. 26) and would give birth to God's son, who would be a king whose rule would last for ever. Mary was told to call her son Jesus.

*John carries a banner bearing Latin words meaning "Behold the Lamb of God"*

*John wears camel-hair clothes, the typical garments of a prophet*

**JOHN THE BAPTIST**
John led the life of a prophet and preacher, encouraging people to repent their sins and be baptized. John's preaching prepared the way for Jesus, and when Jesus grew up he asked John to baptize him in the River Jordan.

Statue by Donatello, 1386–1466

**GLAD TIDINGS**
Luke's account of the nativity describes how angels appeared to shepherds in the fields just outside Bethlehem. The angels told them the good news of Jesus' birth and the shepherds came down from the fields into the town to worship the newborn king. This story shows that Jesus is important to everyone, even "outsiders" like the shepherds.

*God looks down from Heaven*

**FOLLOW THE STAR**
Matthew's Gospel tells how magi, or wise men, followed a star from the east to Jerusalem in search of a child born to rule the people of Israel. King Herod sent them to Bethlehem, where they found Jesus.

14th-century pendant showing the magi with Jesus

Gold

Frankincense

Myrrh

**FIT FOR A KING**
The magi worshipped Jesus and gave him three gifts: gold, frankincense, and myrrh. The symbolism of these gifts may be interpreted in different ways. One interpretation is that gold represents riches, frankincense kingship, and myrrh a special spiritual calling.

*The shepherds watch their flocks of sheep*

15th-century stained glass from Ulm Cathedral in Germany

**ROYAL RIVALRY**
King Herod ruled the Holy Land on behalf of the Romans. According to Matthew, he tried to destroy Jesus, whom he saw as a rival to his throne. Herod told his men to kill all the children in Bethlehem who were less than two years old. God warned Joseph of this, and he escaped with Mary and Jesus to Egypt.

*Mary, her husband Joseph, and the baby Jesus*

Glazed earthenware altarpiece made by Giovanni della Robbia, 1521

# The teachings of Jesus

**FISHERS OF MEN**
As this Italian mosaic shows, Andrew and Simon were fishermen. Jesus called them to be his disciples, telling them that, if they followed him, he would teach them to catch people (enlist new followers of Christ) instead of fish.

JESUS' MINISTRY – his period of teaching – probably lasted no more than three years, but it had an enormous impact. During this short time he preached, taught, and performed miracles in the Holy Land, especially in the villages around the Sea of Galilee. Jesus was a brilliant teacher who could explain things in ways that everyone could understand. His teachings attracted many followers because they revealed a new way of looking at God's kingdom. He said it was open to all believers who would turn away from their sins, including the poor, the sick, and social outcasts.

**GOD'S OWN SON**
The Gospels describe how, when Jesus was baptized (p. 58), the Holy Spirit came down like a dove and God's voice was heard saying, "This is my own dear Son". This momentous event, shown here in a 5th-century mosaic from Ravenna in Italy, marks the beginning of Jesus' ministry.

**HUMBLE LEADER**
Jesus called 12 disciples to be his special companions. They were expected to leave their families and possessions to follow and help Jesus, and carry on his work after his death. When he washed the disciples' feet, as shown on this French manuscript, Jesus was showing them that they should be as humble as their leader.

*Jesus turns water into wine at Cana*

*Jesus on the cross surrounded by Roman soldiers and the two Marys*

**A LIFE IN GLASS**
This window from St Albans Cathedral in Hertfordshire, England, shows key episodes from the life of Jesus. It includes his baptism, the water into wine miracle, and the crucifixion. The bottom right-hand panel of the window shows Jesus as a shepherd, a symbol of the way in which he cared for the people around him.

Paying the tax collector

**TAX COLLECTORS**
Some members of a Jewish group called the Pharisees tried to trick Jesus into criticizing the Roman authorities. They asked him whether it was right that they should pay taxes to the Romans. Jesus showed them the emperor's portrait on the coins and said that they should give the emperor what belonged to him.

**CALMING WATERS**
Jesus grew up in Nazareth, but moved to Capernaum, on the banks of the Sea of Galilee, where he began his ministry. Jesus did much of his teaching in this region, and one of his miracles was the calming of a storm on the lake's waters. When he wanted a quiet place to pray, Jesus travelled into the local hills, which can be seen in the background of this photograph of the Sea of Galilee's northern shore.

at His understanding and answers
To the Glory of God and in memory of Joseph Parsons who died 15 Oct. 1849.

by loving-kindness and mercy shall follow me all the days of my life
Erected by his grand-daughter, Lilian Lizette Nicholls 1939.

**FEEDING THE MULTITUDE**
This is the only miracle described in all four of the Gospels. After a long day's preaching, Jesus and the disciples wished to rest, but they were followed by a vast crowd who wanted to hear Jesus speak. Jesus felt sorry that the crowd had no food, and produced enough for all of them from the only available foodstuffs – five small loaves and two fishes.

# The miracles

The Gospels describe more than 30 of Jesus' miracles. Some of these involved feeding the needy, others were "nature miracles", such as calming the storm or walking on the water. But the majority involved some sort of healing – either curing people of physical diseases like leprosy and paralysis or "casting out demons" to rid people of mental illness. The Gospels record three occasions when Jesus even raised people from the dead.

**WATER INTO WINE**
Jesus' first miracle, which is described in John's Gospel, took place at a wedding that he attended at Cana in Galilee. When the wine ran out, Jesus told the servants to fill six large pots with water, and when they poured the liquid out of the pots it had turned into wine. The wine was so good that the guests thought the bridegroom had kept the best until last.

Terracotta jars for storing water

*Continued on next page*

Continued from previous page

# Parables and lessons

Jesus' favourite way of teaching was to use parables – short stories that make their point by means of a simple comparison. Jesus used these parables to talk about the kingdom of God, and to illustrate how people should behave towards each other. Jesus also preached moral lectures called sermons. The most famous of these was the Sermon on the Mount, in which he explained the key features of the kingdom of God (p. 26) and the Christian way of life. Above all, Jesus said that you should "Do for others what you want them to do for you".

**THE LOST SON**
This parable tells of a man who divided his wealth between his two sons. The younger son went off and spent his share, while his brother worked hard at home. When the younger son returned, his father killed his prize calf for a celebratory feast. The elder son objected, but his father said, "He was lost, but now he has been found". These Chinese illustrations show the story from the handing over of the money to the family feast.

19th-century window of the Good Samaritan

**THE GOOD SAMARITAN**
Jesus taught that you should love your neighbour. When someone asked Jesus, "Who is my neighbour?" he told this story: A man was robbed and left for dead. A Jewish priest and a Levite passed, but did not help. Then a Samaritan – a member of a group scorned by the Jews – came by. He helped the injured man and took him to safety. The Samaritan was the true neighbour.

**SERMON ON THE MOUNT**
In this sermon Jesus said that members of God's kingdom should try to achieve the perfection shown by God. For example, he explained that it is not enough simply to obey the commandment, "Do not commit murder". Christians should avoid anger completely.

*The disciples have haloes, to indicate their holiness*

Sower's bag and seeds

**PLANTING WORDS**
Jesus compared his words to seeds scattered by a farmer. Some of the seed fell on the path and was stepped on. Some fell on rocky ground or among thorn bushes, where seedlings could not grow. Finally, some fell on good soil and grew into corn. Jesus said that people who heard and understood his words were like the good soil.

Figs and fig leaf

**LESSON OF THE FIG TREE**
Jesus told people to think of a fig tree. When its leaves start to appear, people know that summer is on its way. Similarly, they should look out for signs of Jesus' second coming. When strange things happen to the moon and stars, when whole countries are in despair, and people are faint from fear, then they will know that the kingdom of God is about to come.

*Jesus would probably have sat down to deliver the sermon*

**THE LORD'S PRAYER**
Jesus gave his most important lesson about prayer in the Sermon on the Mount. He told his listeners not to pray ostentatiously with long, elaborate prayers – God knows what you need before you ask. Instead, he gave them the *Lord's Prayer* beginning, "Our Father in Heaven, hallowed be your name…". It has been translated into languages as diverse as Spanish and Chinese, and is repeated in Christian churches the world over.

Pater noster qui es in caelis
Sanctificetur nomen tuum
Adveniat regnum tuum
Fiat voluntas tua sicut in
caelo et in terra Panem
nostrum quotidianum da nobis
hodie Et dimitte nobis de
bita nostra sicut et nos dim
ittimus debitoribus nostris
Et ne nos inducas in temp
tatione Sed libera nos
a malo Amen

Horn book with the text of the *Lord's Prayer* in Latin

15th-century fresco by Fra Angelico

Common poppies

*"Happy are those who are merciful to others; God will be merciful to them! Happy are the pure in heart; they will see God!"*

**MATTHEW 5:7–8**
Jesus' Sermon on the Mount

**FLOWERY FINERY**
During the Sermon on the Mount, Jesus told his listeners that they should not care too much about everyday things like food and clothes. Wild flowers do not have fine garments, but they are still beautifully dressed. People should be concerned with God's kingdom, not with possessions or finery.

# The crucifixion

JESUS WARNED HIS DISCIPLES several times that he would soon die. He told them that the Jewish chief priests would reject him, that he would be killed, and that he would rise again after three days. The disciples failed to understand these warnings, and were unprepared for what happened when Jesus went to Jerusalem. Jesus was put on trial and condemned to death on the cross. This is the most solemn part of the Christian story, but it is also the major turning point – Christians believe Jesus' blood was spilt so that they could be granted eternal life with God.

**ENTRY INTO JERUSALEM**
Jesus rode into Jerusalem on a donkey, as shown in this painting from the Oratory of Saint Pellegrino in Italy. Many people laid down palm leaves, or even their coats, to cover the dusty path in front of him. They were happy because the prophet Zechariah had predicted that their king would arrive on a donkey.

**BODY AND BLOOD**
At the last supper with his disciples, Jesus broke the bread and told them to eat it, saying, "This is my body". He then gave them the wine, saying, "This is my blood". When Christians celebrate Communion (pp. 52–53) they remember or recreate these events.

*Jesus is shown with the marks of the nails in his palms*

*Christ looks triumphant, not suffering*

**ON THE CROSS**
In Jesus' time crucifixion was the normal way in which the Romans imposed the death sentence. Jesus was crucified between two criminals, and the Gospels recall that his death took about three hours – much faster than usual. At the point of Jesus' death the curtain in the Temple in Jerusalem was torn in two and an earthquake shook the ground.

10th-century crucifix from Denmark, made of gilded carved oak

Rosary medal showing Jesus carrying his cross